Make Music With

Crowded House

Complete Lyrics / Guitar Chord Boxes / Chord Symbols
Eighteen classic songs with a foreword by Stevie Chick

Published 2002

© International Music Publications Ltd
Griffin House 161 Hammersmith Road London W6 8BS England

Editor: Chris Harvey
Foreword: Stevie Chick
Design: Dominic Brookman
Music arranged and engraved by: Artemis Music Ltd
Cover Photograph © 2002 Patrick Ford / Redferns Music Picture Library
All other photography © 2002 Glenn A Baker Archives, Patrick Ford, Gems, Suzi Gibbons, Bob King, Michel Linssen
and Ebet Roberts / Redferns Music Picture Library

Discography:Albums

Crowded House (Capitol Records)

Mean To Me
World Where You Live
Now We're Getting Somewhere
Don't Dream It's Over
Love You 'Til The Day I Die
Something So Strong
Hole In The River
Can't Carry On
I Walk Away
Tombstone
That's What I Call Love

UK Release Date: April 1986

Temple of Low Men (Capitol Records)

I Feel Possessed
Kill Eye
Into Temptation
Mansion In The Slums
When You Come
Never Be The Same
Love This Life
Sister Madly
In The Lowlands
Better Be Home Soon

UK Release Date: August 1988

Woodface (Capitol Records)

Chocolate Cake
It's Only Natural
Fall At Your Feet
Tall Trees
Weather With You
Whispers And Moans
Four Seasons In One Day
There Goes God
Fame Is
All I Ask
As Sure As I Am
Italian Plastic
She Goes On
How Will You Go?
We're Still Here

UK Release Date: June 1991
Highest Chart Position: 6
Weeks On Chart: 86

Together Alone (Capitol Records)

Kare Kare
In My Command
Nails In My Feet
Black & White Boy
Fingers Of Love
Pineapple Head
Locked Out
Private Universe
Walking On The Spot
Distant Sun
Catherine Wheels
Skin Feeling
Together Alone

UK Release Date: October 1993
Highest Chart Position: 4
Weeks On Chart: 32

Recurring Dream: The Very Best Of Crowded House (Capitol Records)

Weather With You
World Where You Live
Fall At Your Feet
Locked Out
Don't Dream It's Over
Into Temptation
Pineapple Head
When You Come
Private Universe
Not The Girl You Think You Are
Instinct
I Feel Possessed
Four Seasons In One Day
It's Only Natural
Distant Sun
Something So Good
Mean To Me
Better Be Home Soon
Everything Is Good For You

UK Release Date: July 1996
Highest Chart Position: 1
Weeks On Chart: 63

Afterglow (Capitol Records)

I Am In Love
Sacred Cow
You Can Touch
Help is coming
I Love You Dawn
Dr Livingstone
My Telly's Gone Bung
Private Universe (demo)
Lester
Anyone Can Tell
Recurring Dream
Left Hand
Time Immemorial

(initial pressings included a bonus CD featuring interview with Neil Finn regarding the rarities project)

UK Release Date: 2000

Discography:Singles

World Where You Live / That's What I Call Love (Capitol CL 416)
UK Release Date: July 1986
Also released as 12"/ CD / Cassingle with ext. mix of *World Where You Live*,
Something So Strong and *Don't Dream Its Over*

Don't Dream It's Over / That's What I Call Love (CL 438)
UK Release Date: January 1987
Highest Chart Position: 27
Weeks On Chart: 8
Also released as 12" / CD / Cassingle with ext. mix of *Don't Dream It's Over*

Better Be Home Soon / Kill Eye (CL 498)
UK Release Date: June 1988
Also released as 12" / CD / Cassingle with *Don't Dream It's Over* (live from
Trocadero, PA, 1987)

Sister Madly / Mansion in the Slums (CL 509)
UK Release Date: August 1988
Also released as 12" / CD / Cassingle with *Something So Strong* (live from
Trocadero, PA, 1987)

Chocolate Cake / As Sure As I Am (CL 618)
UK Release Date: June 1991
Highest Chart Position: 69
Weeks On Chart: 2
Also released as 12" / CD single with *Anyone Can Tell*

Fall At Your Feet / Don't Dream It's Over (CL 626)
UK Release Date: October 1991
Highest Chart Position: 17
Weeks On Chart: 7
Also released as 12" / CD single with *Six Months in A Leaky Boat* (live) and
Now We're Getting Somewhere (live)

Weather With You (single edit) / *Into Temptation* (CL 643)
UK Release Date: February 1992
Highest Chart Position: 7
Weeks On Chart: 9
Also released over 2 CD singles: (CDCL 643) with *Mr. Tambourine Man*, *Eight
Miles High*, and *So You Want to Be A Rock'n'Roll Star* (live with Roger
McGuinn at The Pantages Theater, Los Angeles, CA, 7 April 1989); and
(CDCLS 643) with *Fall At Your Feet*, *When You Come*, and *Walking on the
Spot* (live at The Town & Country Club, London, England, 9 and 10 November
1991).

Four Seasons In One Day / There Goes God (CL 655)
UK Release Date: June 1992
Highest Chart Position: 26
Weeks On Chart: 5
Also released over 2 CD singles: (CDCL 655) with *Dr. Livingstone*, *Recurring
Dream* (1989 vers.) and *Anyone Can Tell*; and (CDCLS 655) with *Weather
With You*, *Italian Plastic* (live at The Town & Country Club, London, England, 9
and 10 November 1991) and *Message to My Girl* (live at the Birmingham Town
Hall, 5 March 1992).

It's Only Natural / Chocolate Cake (CL 661)
UK Release Date: September 1992
Highest Chart Position: 24
Weeks On Chart: 4
Also released over 2 CD singles: (CDCLS 661) with *It's Only Natural* (live at
Sheffield City Hall), *Hole In the River* (live at Cambridge Corn Exchange) and
The Burglar's Song (medley, live); and (CDCL 661) with *Sister Madly* (Live at
Newcastle City Hall), *There Goes God* (live at Brigham Centre) and *Chocolate
Cake* (live at Wolverhampton Civic Hall)

Distant Sun
UK Release Date: October 1993
Highest Chart Position: 19
Weeks On Chart: 6
Released as 2 CD singles: (CDCLS 697) with *This Is Massive* and *When You
Come* (Live at Roxy, 1987); and (CDCL 697) with *Throw Your Arms* and *One
Step Ahead* (Live at Roxy, 1987).

Nails In My Feet
UK Release Date: November 1993
Highest Chart Position: 22
Weeks On Chart: 4
Released as 2 CD singles: (CDCLS 701) with *You Can Touch* and *Zen Roxy*;
and *Four Seasons In One Day* (live from the parking lot Capitol Records CA
1991) and *I Am In Love*.

Locked Out
UK Release Date: February 1994
Highest Chart Position: 12
Weeks On Chart: 4
Released as 2 CD singles: (CDCLS 707) with *Distant Sun*, *Hole In The River*
and *Sister Madly* (live) and (CDCL 707) with *Private Universe*, *Fall At Your Feet*
and *Better Be Home Soon* (live).

Fingers Of Love
UK Release Date: June 1994
Highest Chart Position: 25
Weeks On Chart: 3
Released as 2 CD singles: (CDCLS 715) with *Kare Kare* and *In My Command*
(live) and *Skin Feeling*; and (CDCL 715) with *Pineapple Head* and *Something
So Strong* (live) and *Catherine Wheels*.

Pineapple Head (CL 723)
UK Release Date: September 1994
Highest Chart Position: 27
Weeks On Chart: 3
Backed with album versions of *Weather With You*, *Don't Dream Its Over* and
Together Alone

Instinct
UK Release Date: June 1996
Highest Chart Position: 12
Weeks On Chart: 4
Released as 2 CD singles: (82962) with *Recurring Dream*, *Weather With You*
and *Chocolate Cake* (live in Newcastle Australia, 1992) and (82963) with *World
Where You Live*, *In the Low Lands* and *Into Temptation* (all live).

Not The Girl You Think You Are
UK Release Date: August 1996
Highest Chart Position: 20
Weeks On Chart: 3
Released as 2 CD singles: (83183) with *Instinct*, *Distant Sun* and *Fall At Your
Feet* (live from Phill Jupitus's GLR radio show, 1996); and (83184) with *Private
Universe*, *Fingers Of Love* and *Better Be Home Soon* (live, from same
session)

Don't Dream Its Over
UK Release Date: November 1996
Highest Chart Position: 25
Weeks On Chart: 2
Released as 2 CD singles: (83341) with *Weather With You*, *Into Temptation*
and *Locked Out* (live from Phill Jupitus's GLR Radio Show, 1996); and (83342)
with *Four Seasons In One Day*, *In My Command* and *Pineapple Head* (live,
from same session)

Foreword

"I really like Crowded House, but I could never admit it. I mean, they're really uncool and MOR."
Neil Finn, sarcastically, to Q Magazine's Stuart Maconie, 1994

Though they might never have troubled the fickle canons of cool, softly softly Crowded House made tuneful, moving, powerful pop music their own throughout the 1980s and 1990s. When their Greatest Hits album (and, to their many fans' dismay, premature swansong) **Recurring Dream** was released at the end of the Summer of 1996, the band had dominated the charts and the radiowaves so absolutely that the collection's stellar playlist was swimming with genuine hits which lived on in many a heart and memory. The previous couple of years had been very good to the band. While they'd enjoyed critical respect and some crossover success since the release of their eponymous debut album, it wasn't until 1991's hugely successful breakthrough release **Woodface** that the songwriting genius of Neil Finn became utterly ubiquitous. Along with its stunning follow-up, 1993's **Together Alone**, the album sold this unique, often eccentric group to the heartlands, with its 'classic' songwriting touches, strong melodies and lyrics, and its deftly textured, timeless grounding in acoustic guitars and strong harmonies.

And while, in that moment, the fiscal security of Crowded House was guaranteed forever, the exchange also seemed to ensure that the band would be short-changed in terms of respect from the critical fraternity. The band effortlessly shifted many a unit thanks to Finn's superb songwriting, mining a seam of brilliantly popular, populist pop music which never sold short the intelligence of his potential audience, managing to echo the inspiration of Lennon & McCartney a good deal sharper and less slavishly than the eminently more revered Noel Gallagher. It's hard not to conclude that Finn's very success ensured the snobbery which would surround the band from their peaks of success to their sudden, saddening demise.

Mistaken for some cosy, comforting woolly jumper of pop, the songs of Crowded House have been taken for granted by rock's criterati, perhaps because there's no kudos in loving something so much a part of popular culture - and truly, no band so dominates on modern AOR-esque radio programming today, nor deserves to. Certainly as mild-mannered a family man as Finn, not given to extremes of ego or bad behaviour, makes for bad copy. Which is a tragedy, not least since Neil Finn the Songwriter is an artist of such deceptive depths, whose soothing songs and mellifluous melodies cloak lyrics which touch upon very real disquiets we all face at some time in our lives. Surely this is one of the essential reasons for Crowded House's enduring success, not just their radio-friendly sound but the emotional succour Finn's songs provide, true blue-eyed, blue-collar soul without any of the contrivance or fakery that description suggests. This also ignores the gentle turbulence which has stirred in Crowded House's heart since they formed, which doubtless precipitated the band's premature split, and which, along the way, inspired their greatest music. This was, for all its childlike simplicity, for all its melodic naiveté and open-hearted optimism, most definitely 'adult' music, and there's very little that's sexy or exciting on the facile level much of the press operates on there.

It was most definitely the press's loss. The world-dominating success of Woodface and the band's other releases prove Finn's skill, as if it were ever in question. But deeper than mere sales figures and airplay charts, the passion with which people clutch Finn's songs to their hearts, the way in which Crowded House's music seamlessly inveigles itself into peoples' lives, the manner in which these tunes have become modern standards, speak with deeper wisdom and surer insight to Finn's art and artistry. **Weather With You** now challenges **Here Comes The Sun** for the top of the tubeway buskers' charts, while many, many more can hum Finn's tunes than could pick him out of a police line-up. Perhaps the relative anonymity of his band in relation to their tunes, or the lack of kudos he received for this wonderful (and still expanding) songbook riled him some, if the title to his first solo collection, 1998's **Try Whistling This**, is to be taken (too) seriously. More likely, **Try Whistling This** was another example of the dry, subtle wit Finn has exercised throughout his career, another wrinkle to ponder on the part of one of pop's most ubiquitous enigmas.

Who is Neil Finn? Who were Crowded House? Difficult questions to answer with any real certainty. The best advice one can offer, perhaps, is simply, try whistling (and playing, and singing) these...

Certainly the creatives who peopled Crowded House's engine room throughout their career weren't about to sell Neil Finn short as some nouveau Easy Listening bard. Mitchell Froom and Tchad Blake may have fashioned the lush, accessible, swelling pop swoons that were the band's first three releases - 1986's Crowded House, 1988's **Temple Of Low Men**, and **Woodface**, along with the three new tracks which were added to **Recurring Dream** - but these men's achievements weren't limited to chiming soul-pop that wins the world's hearts with laughable ease. When not working with Crowded House (or Paul McCartney, or Sheryl Crow, etc etc), producer / engineer team Froom and Blake could be found working with some of pop's more esoteric, leftfield talents, like new-wave poetess Laurie Anderson or Japanese avant-pop duo Cibo Mato.

Indeed, Blake supervised the recording of Pearl Jam's 2000 album Binaural, much of which incorporated the experimental 'Binaural' recording system, which attempted to replicate the natural stereo effect of a listener's two ears via microphones embedded in a replica human head. While this experimentalism wasn't necessarily obviously apparent in Crowded House's music, it certainly adds a further level of complexity to their recorded output. As for Youth, who took the band to the beach of Kare Kare to record **Together Alone**, his history lay in bleak proto-industrial post-punks Killing Joke and Blue Pearl, the dance collective responsible for rave hit **Naked In The Rain** - not the curriculum vitae one might expect for a man who would forge Crowded House's last album.

But then, Neil Finn's own musical roots weren't as pure or straightforward as Crowded House's music might suggest. While the 'House's rightly-legendary live shows were marked by a giddy, joyful sense of humour and an anarchy which resulted in impromptu songs, unlikely cover versions and, with alarming regularity, paper aeroplane heckles from the audience, their essence was never one of showy extroversion or pretension.

In the best possible way, exactly the opposite was true of Split Enz, the Auckland, New Zealand art-rock combo whose abstruse but eminently winning wizardry stretched through the seventies to the early eighties, and who, in a roundabout way, delivered us Crowded House. Formed in 1972, they were fronted by a young Tim Finn, Neil's elder brother, and were marked out by their eccentricity, their art-school playfulness, their drama-college showiness, but mostly their propensity towards costumes and crazy haircuts. At the band's heart lay Tim Finn's songwriting: archer, more complex than his brother's style, suiting his more edgy, bohemian persona, but still blessed with an irresistible tunefulness which shone through the more oddball tendencies of his band.

Of course, the mid-1970s were a great time to be an arty, experimental outfit with a strong image, and so the Enz's decision to move to London and record with Phil Manzanera of the similarly outré, extravagant Roxy Music certainly made a bizarre sense. But the experiment didn't yield the commercial success all parties wished for; in the interim, punk-rock had gripped the UK, and the nation's ear wasn't quite in the mood for the multicoloured peacock-coiffeur prog-pop Split Enz held in their arsenal. The experience saw the original line-up dissolve, but the kernel of the Enz's salvation was in this dark moment. For, in late 1976, Finn the elder sent word to his younger brother Neil to augment the line-up, initiating a creative partnership that would, intermittently, stretch throughout Neil's entire career, and which would have a powerful effect on the fortunes of Crowded House. The effect Neil's addition to the ranks would have upon Split Enz wasn't instantly felt, but it would both make and, ultimately, break the band. **I Got You**, a single from the band's 1979 album **True Colors** penned by Finn, would go on to make momentary international stars of the band, a huge radio hit which served the band well on the nascent MTV network.

Edgy but infectious, **I Got You** eschewed Split Enz's previous eclecticism for a skewed but relatively straight-ahead pop sensibility. Indeed, it's archetypal Neil Finn, despite the rinky-dink keyboard motifs which tie the record somewhat to the brash new wave era it hails from. All the tricks Neil would later explore in Crowded House are present here, from the nagging melody, to the explosive and unforgettable hook (the recurrent descending lines of the chorus). Added to that is the deft lyric, a tale of an uncertain lover's anxiety - "I don't know why sometimes I get frightened / You can see my eyes and tell that I'm not lying" - giving the song a powerful, universal emotional kick.

The success of **I Got You** secured Split Enz international record deals, and shifted over 200,000 copies in Australia alone, equivalent to one copy in every 10 homes. However, none of the five studio albums the band would release over the following half-decade would repeat the success of **True Colors**. Meanwhile, Neil's expanded status within the band caused friction between the brothers, Tim feeling overshadowed by the success of Neil's songs. The group's penultimate offering, 1983's **Conflicting Emotions** saw Neil pen the lion's share of the songs. By the following year's studio

swansong, **See Ya Around**, Tim had left the band.

But the seeds for Neil's future had been sown in the closing moments of Split Enz. For the band's last album, Paul Hester was welcomed onboard as drummer. And while sticksmen are often unfairly chided for their influence on the bands they steer, Hester would make up an essential third of the band the world would come to know and love as Crowded House.

"They thought I was a bit of an inner-city socialite and I don't think they liked the way I dressed. But I mean, they wore slippers and cardigans and I never said anything about it."
    Nick Seymour, to Who Magazine's Alix Clark, on first meeting Paul and Neil

It was at a farewell party for Split Enz that the core trio of Crowded House first congregated, where - slightly the worse for alcoholic wear - future bassist Nick Seymour approached Paul and Neil (from that evening on effectively unemployed) and let them know, in no uncertain terms, that he wouldn't be averse to joining them in any further musical endeavours.

Despite the maudlin nature of the evening's events, such future ventures were definitely on Finn's mind that night. Just because Split Enz, his first band, had run aground, didn't mean he was remotely ready to hang up his spurs yet. "Paul had just joined the band and he was about my age," remembered Neil to Musician magazine around the time of **Woodface's** release. "I began to revel in the idea of having a small group of guys about my age." The subtext was clear: Crowded House - though always at heart a democracy, where each member held as much sway over the final sound as the others - would be Neil's band in a way Split Enz never really had been. There would be none of the squabbles over songwriting which had marred the last days of Split Enz, or so Neil thought.

They started life as The Mullanes, drawing their monicker from Neil's own middle name. Even though the band were still half-formed, with a second guitarist, Craig Hooper, filling out the ranks, Seymour would go on to remark that there was an "instinctive, intuitive chemistry between us from day one." A special band indeed. At the beginning of the Summer of 1985, the band - now minus Hooper - travelled to Los Angeles, demos in hand, to shop for a record deal, signing to Capitol Records - one-time home of Finn's beloved Beatles. The label had two fortuitous stipulations in mind before the ink on the contract dried, however. Firstly, the band would have to change their name, to Crowded House. Secondly, that they would work with Mitchell Froom, a then-relatively unknown producer/musician who would become a key element in the Crowded House story.

The band stayed in Los Angeles to record their debut album, with Froom working closely with the band to hone their sound so it might best please the American market the band were now being explicitly aimed at. Not that there was anything in the nascent Finn songbook which might alienate American audiences: the songs he presented Froom and the band with were the product of a healthy, catholic record collection, evoking memories of sources as eclectic as The Everly Brothers, Motown and, of course, the so-called British Invasion of the 1960s, bands like The Kinks, The Who, The Move and, especially, The Beatles, whose guitar-led, heavy pop sensibilities has hijacked American airwaves in that golden decade, and in whose image the whole concept of 'classic pop' seemed to have been hewn. The contrast between these songs and the sometimes self-conscious, intensely playful tunes which had peppered Split Enz's catalogue was obvious and keenly felt.

These weren't songs which wore their intellect or their creativity on their sleeves. Finn was writing and playing from the heart this time - though as the tart, wry **Mean To Me**, from Crowded House proved, Finn wasn't above slipping the odd sly wink among the sweetly arranged heartache - and the power of these songs would be in this ease of communication between songwriter and audience, the spell Finn's words and melodies would soon hold over his fans.

First of all, however, Froom had to shoehorn these songs into a format which would please radio programmers of the mid 1980s. A decade now generally accepted as a dark age where substance often ran a poor second to style, where the flash and pizzazz that flecked the era drowned out the music, the 1980s was the decade of blue-eyed soul gone crazy, of synthesisers and drum machines replacing real musicians, of the airless, heartless, studio-tweaked records. How would an act as essentially organic as Crowded House fit in this peculiarly skewed market?

Froom's tactic was to subtly shade Finn's stripped-bare tunefulness with keyboards, layered guitars, even Stax-esque horn bursts. On this first album, the production is instinctive and yet complex, Froom shading each song differently, accentuating different elements and qualities of each individual

track. And nowhere is Froom's expertise better felt than in **Don't Dream It's Over**, the single which initially sold Crowded House to the world.

Perhaps the most overtly, obviously 'soulful' song in the Crowded House catalogue (and later covered, note for note in a somewhat pointless exercise, by 80s British pop/soul pretender Paul Young), this glorious, slow-burning ballad drips with unforgettable melodies. The swelling overdubbed harmonies whispering "Hey now, hey now," are perhaps the most instant and powerful hook in the song, feeling like some glorious gospel chorus wrapping its arms around you in reassurance. But Froom placed other elements from the soul genre in the mix - the poignant Hammond organ counter-melody in the solo section seemingly drifting in from some Hi Records/Memphis-soul bolt hole. Then there's the gentle, lazy three-note guitar riff which repeats throughout the song, lapping away like the tide, helping to piece together the gloriously unhurried, calming quality of the song, not to mention one of Finn's finest ever vocal performances, movingly straining for notes mostly absent from the rest of Crowded House's oeuvre.

It doesn't hurt that the song contains some of Finn's best lyrics as well. Continuing the gospel/soul thread, it's a song of reassurance, a paean to looking to the future, away from the problems that plague the moment and towards the resolution the next day might bring. And yet there's an expert Finn touch in the sense of doubt which shadows the song. "There's a battle ahead, many battles are lost," sings Finn, obliquely referencing the severity of the trials he and his partner face, adding "But you'll never see the end of the road if you're travelling with me". It's the bittersweetness of the reassurance, this twist, that gives the song its power. And notice the slight change in the final lines of the chorus as the song progresses: "We know they won't win," he sings in the first instance; as the song fades out, Finn is pleading, "Don't ever let them win," revealing the chinks in his own armour, his own faith, at the last moment. It's a trick Finn employed on Split Enz's **I Got You**, switching the last lines of that chorus from "You can tell that I'm not lying" to "I can tell that you're not mine," embodying the insecurity which marked the entire song. **Don't Dream It's Over** was the breakthrough single for both Crowded House the band and the album, peaking at number 2 in the Billboard charts, but not without some pretty unusual promotional activities on the part of the band. Turning down initial plans for a long, exhaustive tour of the United States - a soul-destroying activity which has pulverised many a worthy young band - Finn and co. opted instead for low-key acoustic shows for industry insiders and, even more peculiarly, playing impromptu sets in restaurants across LA. They also performed whenever they could on network television, where the wit and charm of the band could be shared with the widest possible audience, their feelgood anarchism seeping across the nation's airwaves.

More hits from the album followed, and why not? It was certainly a strong collection, many of the songs remaining staples in the band's legendarily circuitous live performances for years. **Something So Strong** is just a stunning slab of upbeat sunshine pop, it's whirling keyboards adding a touch of Van Morrison-esque celtic soul. Fittingly, it's a love song about love itself, more than any particular passion. And yet, as ever, in the midst of the positivism, the reverie, Finn can't help but nod towards the darkness on the edge of town. "Love can make you weep," he sings, "Love can leave you cold". These glimpses of pain are slipped in to make us savour the good moments that little bit more, perhaps, or to let us know that, even when singing of love in the abstract, Finn senses the heartbreak as surely as the glory. For **Now We're Getting Somewhere**, however, the trick is reversed. This time, the uncertainty isn't in the background, it's the subject. And, suitably, Finn's melody is muted, darker. The hope in the other songs is still there, but this time it's problematic, compromised almost. "It never used to be that bad / But neither was it great," sings Finn, in this expertly observed distillation of a relationship mouldering through disinterest or just simply fizzling out through the rigours of time. The closing lines embody this sadness, and also a desperation to make it work somehow, anyhow. "There is pain in my heart," sings Finn, "We choose what we choose to believe." It's a startlingly dark closing line.

But the personal nature of many of these first songs wasn't always so downbeat. One of the strongest tunes on the album was **World Where You Live**, not least for its wonderful, stirring chorus, well-served by Froom's rambunctious, almost-blustery production which was very much in tune with its times. It's a song of displacement, and doubtless comes right from the heart of these intelligent Antipodeans, as they face the bizarre parade that is life in the city of dreams. "We're strangers here," sings Finn, with very little regret.

The success of Crowded House gave the band a renewed confidence, but the task of following up their initial stateside success would prove a trial again for Finn, as it had for Split Enz after **I Got You** opened the figurative door for that band.

After the band's final split in 1996, bassist Nick Seymour would later describe the period spent writing and recording what became **Temple Of Low Men** as his favourite, because "Neil wasn't fighting against success". Indeed not, since this album was a pitched struggle against much darker circumstances; but it was a heroic fight, and one with an enduring final reward. **Temple Of Low Men** might not have sold as many copies as the rest of the Crowded House catalogue, nor sired the smash singles the other records enjoyed, but it's regarded by both critics and hardcore Crowded House fans as perhaps their finest, most mature work. Bleak in places, and with the crossover-smash-single largely absent from its tracklisting, Finn instead tackled more personal, harrowing subjects, his songwriting prowess having grown considerably with the experience of the band's first album.

Spirits were high amongst the band during the sessions, as evidenced by the album's in-production title, **Mediocre Follow-Up**. Froom and Blake were back in place, though this time their production style was, in sympathy with the material, lacking the more superficial sparkle of the previous release. This record would be characterised by almost-suffocating, swelling strings, couching a suite of songs by Finn coloured with self-doubt and disquiet.

One of the most enduring songs from this excellent collection was **Into Temptation**, a powerful observation of the beginnings of an extra-marital affair, steeped in guilt and potential recrimination and yet ever mindful of the seductive sense that leads to the sin. The melody's minor inflections are slow, winding, mournful, reproachful even; the orchestration is sumptuous, billowing, forbidding. Not typical radio fodder, perhaps, like the rest of the album it sacrifices the easy sheen, the surface comfort, to touch deeper.

Which is where **Love This Life** comes in, the sole selection from **Temple Of Low Men** appearing in this book, and a firm favourite amongst Crowded House fandom (there's even an internet listerv for the fans to discuss all things Crowded and Housed named after a line from the track, **Tongue In The Mail**). One of the bleakest moments in the Finn songbook, it sums up perfectly the sombre toned melancholic pop of this album, bitter at first taste but with a compulsive quality, and a depth beyond the sparkling pop of the first album.

While the album *was* well received critically and by the fans, what **Temple Of Low Men** most emphatically did *not* do was expand the band's fanbase. The lack of a prospective hit single was key to this situation: although the fine, slow-burning **Better Be Home Soon**, one of the few upbeat tracks on this most satisfyingly gloomy of excursions, was selected for release, it stalled outside of the top 40. A prospective three month US tour was cancelled as a result, and after a short but successful tour of Canada and Australasia, the band went on indefinite hiatus.

It took a certain X-Factor to spin the Crowded House chemistry into the inspired overdrive which delivered Woodface - the band's most universally loved, best sold album - to a grateful world. Ironically, that elusive element was the man whose eccentricity, whose creative restlessness and playfulness made Split Enz the band they were - a beloved but eternally cultish attraction, held close to the hearts of a special few but mostly ignored by the world at large. What exactly was it that prompted such a reversal in Tim Finn's fate, that saw his touch send Crowded House from effective one-hit wonders into the radiowave-swallowing easy-pop monsters they became after this record?

And how strange a crossover album is **Woodface**? An utter curate's egg, the formless jumble of styles and moods which makes up Crowded House's greatest seller - holding together but only just, like a favourite mixtape might - was the result of two separate sets of sessions. Half the album was made up of songs written and recorded for the mooted third Crowded House album; the other half dated from sessions the Finn brothers recorded after a particularly fertile period writing together around the birth of Neil's second son. The pair had never written together so fluidly, so easily. Songs were coming to them in hours, they were progressing at a pace of two songs a day. However, before Neil could commit to this project with his brother, he was honourbound to work on the next Crowded House album. At the close of the sessions, however, Neil felt dissatisfied. Sure, the songs they'd completed were *good*; but he couldn't shake the memory of the music he'd written with his brother the months previous. "There was a slightly dissatisfying feeling about the whole thing," he told Musician magazine, when the album finally surfaced. "These other songs were sitting in an 'untouchable' basket, and to me it all felt like the same thing. Finally I came to the conclusion that maybe it *should* be the same thing."

And so, after pursuing a solo career with admitted limited success since leaving Split Enz, Tim Finn joined Crowded House, as singer/ songwriter/ keyboard player. Anyone who knew the Finn brothers' past history knew the partnership might not last for too long, but when the split finally did come, in

November of 1991, the album this momentary pairing gave the world justified any subsequent tensions within the band.

It must be said, however, that the musical climate was ready for Crowded House to break through when they did with **Woodface**. Only a few months previous to **Fall At Your Feet**'s stunning chart success and radio ubiquity, R.E.M. had pulled off a similar feat with the similarly downbeat **Losing My Religion**. **Fall At Your Feet** - a return to the soulful balladry of **Don't Dream Its Over**, while retaining the glimmer of darkness which made **Temple Of Low Men** such a rewarding listen - is rich with the typical conflicts that pepper Finn's songwriting.

The tensions here arise from the sense of giving oneself to another, questions of vulnerability and loss of self appearing again and again. "I think that I'm beginning to know her," sings Finn, as his protagonist and the lady in question reveal their frailties to each other, while the recurring image of falling at her feet, for shelter, for salvation, is a very powerful one, with all the quasi-religious overtones one might expect from good (lapsed) Catholic boys like Neil Finn. The sensitivity one has come to expect from Finn's lyricism is also present, in the refrain, "Go / I'll be waiting for your call": having seen his lover reveal the darker part of herself, Finn's protagonist knows not to blunder in with well-meaning solutions, but merely to tacitly offer support when needed.

Woodface is a record characterised by bizarre shifts of mood, so we zip along from this moment of rare tenderness to the sarcastic bile of **Chocolate Cake**, the opening track and the song most obviously bearing the handiwork of Finn the Elder. Making explicit the reeling reaction to American culture registered by these New Zealand boys on **World Where You Live**, **Chocolate Cake** rides a choppy Beatles-circa-Revolver groove while splattering waterbombs of pointed wit at such deserving targets as Andrew Lloyd Webber, disgraced televangelist-wife Tammy Baker and America's cult of obesity. There's no churning angst or bitter recriminations here, this song is played purely for laughs, a stinging reminder of Tim Finn's sharp wit and a slightly embittered attack on a nation's relentless gluttony.

The Finn pairing also delivered two of the band's most enduring hits, both using the climate as a metaphor for mood and emotion. **Weather With You** has since become the band's trademark, but again its a relatively light-hearted song for this most complex of bands. The mood here is one of playfulness, the Finns piecing together seemingly-nonsense lyrics (dig the post-modern referencing of classic climate-as-metaphor song **Stormy Weather** in the opening line) and running them over some of the most exquisite sunshine pop Crowded House ever recorded. Listen to the chiming lead guitar part which waxes poetic throughout the song, and you'll hear echoes of the quicksilver folk-rock fusion of prime Byrds; a comparison emboldened by the live tracks included as B-Sides for the single release of the song, covers of Byrds hits recorded in the company of Roger McGuinn himself.

The second weather-based tune was the markedly more bittersweet **Four Seasons In One Day**, an exquisite example of perfectly-paced chamber pop. In both its lyrics and its music, it carried the essence of Crowded House's assuredly adult pop nous, a nakedly honest admission of fallibility and mixed emotions on the part of the Finns' narrator. "Finding out wherever there is comfort / There is pain, one step away" reasons Finn in the closing chorus; it's an unsettling revelation, one which comes with maturity and experience, but placed in the context of this most cherishably orchestrated pocket-symphony - perhaps the album's most explicitly Beatle-esque moment, echoing **Eleanor Rigby** - it's almost comforting.

But it wasn't just the band's gift for enticing miserablism which made **Woodface** such a success. In **It's Only Natural**, the Finns carved one of their sweetest, least angst-fuelled pop songs, characterised by its lovely, lazy guitar line, featherlight harmonies and charming lyrics which pose a paean to enduring romantic love. "You've seen me at my worst / and it won't be the last time I'm down here," sings Neil. Ordinarily, this would be followed by all manner of recrimination and regret, but the sentiment here is decidedly glass-half-full. "Ice will melt, water will boil," run the opening lines - this is a song of love free from doubt, unusual subject matter for Crowded House, and all the sweeter because of it.

And so it was, after the tsunami of success which followed **Woodface** died down, that Crowded House shuffled their creative cards before recording the follow-up. It was a brave decision, given the strength of the band's working relationship with Froom and Blake, but the risk paid off. The changes Youth wrought in the band's writing and recording processes brought a looser, more atmospheric quality to what became their final album proper, and perhaps the finest record of their careers.

Recording in sterile studios in Melbourne or LA was now off the menu. No, Youth wanted the band to up sticks and camp out on the beach of Kare Kare, recording on a mobile studio Youth had hooked up on this remote part of New Zealand. "We tended to look out of the windows and the day dictated the music," remembered Finn, later. "If we were working on a really up, frothy, happy song and it was a moody overcast day we'd be forced to change and do something like **Private Universe** or **Fingers Of Love**. It was an adventure in itself. A worthy way to spend two months." Unlike previous albums, every detail of each song *wouldn't* be painstakingly worked out beforehand; indeed, many songs grew from jam sessions between the musicians (the band were joined by touring guitarist Mark Hart for this album) and the whole band share writing credits on the opening track.

Kare Kare is a sprawling (though never less than enthralling) excursion which drew its strengths from its loose arrangement and its crescendos. The dream-like lyrics, too, took on a mystical bent which had rarely been apparent, almost certainly thanks to the influence of the hippy Brit who was now twiddling the band's figurative knobs. Neil spoke at the time of looking for indigenous forms of expression, tapping into ancient cultures; a Maori choir provided sublime backing vocals on the sumptuous closing title track, while Finn himself referenced Celtic, pagan histories in interviews (the band would later headline the annual Fleadh festival in Finsbury Park).

But **Together Alone** signalled other changes in the Crowded House sound. The guitars were rougher, looser, and the band 'rocked-out' with a spirit and fire the earlier Froom productions had never countenanced. Take the rambunctious **Locked Out**, for example, riding a subtly-funky riff and some earache guitar breaks, one of the noisier moments in the band's catalogue. And **Distant Sun** - perhaps the most charming example of textbook Neil Finn pop - radiated a ragged brilliance, its chiming guitar hooks unravelling with a newfound warmth. It helped that the song - the lead single from **Together Alone** - boasted a lyric that was classic Finn, a potent cocktail of doubt and hope with Finn signing off with the line "I don't pretend to know what you want / But I offer love".

The album also revisited the intoxicating melancholia of **Temple Of Low Men**, taken a notch further by Youth's lush, loose production. The brooding **Fingers Of Love** was one song which benefited from the process of jamming which preceded the sessions; unhurried, atmospheric, the song unfurls with Hart's repeated, stricken guitar-hook and mysterious percussion shudders in the background, as Finn muses on an almost narcotic, protecting love. Meanwhile, a dark dreaminess characterises **Nails In My Feet**, baroque off-kilter verses slipping into warm choruses and a truly spine-tingling guitar solo, while Finn sings of displacement and a "savage review" and the love whose

"It struck me that the combination with Mitchell Froom, although I have nothing but good things say about him, had become a little stale and conservative. I was sick of being called a well crafted, well-mannered pop group."   Neil Finn, to Q Magazine's Stuart Maconie, 1994

skin is "like water on a burning beach". Neil's metaphors hit upon a definite leftfield lucidity with this album.

But he can't take credit for **Pineapple Head**, the title stemming from words burbled by his young son Liam in the midst of a fever. The rest of the song - set to a charming, mandolin-led waltz, sounding like an out-take from Woodface - is seemingly similarly nonsensical, but an interview Finn gave Q's David Hepworth in 1994 shed light on his lyrical approach. "I grew up realising that the songs that I enjoyed, there were maybe a two or three lines that I hooked into and I didn't think of them in a literal sense at all. They just put me into a different state and also made have other thoughts... describ[ing] something I've always felt but never been able to verbalise myself."
Fusing the confidence and melodicism of **Woodface** with the darker tones of **Temple Of Low Men**, Crowded House had crafted their masterpiece in **Together Alone**. But it was to be their final chapter.

In 1994, halfway through a gruelling tour of the United States (where the band enjoyed respect but nothing like the commercial appreciation enjoyed by the eponymous debut), drummer Paul Hester quit the band, to spend more time with his new family. Although the band continued to tour, Hester's absence was keenly felt, not least since he was responsible for the lion's share of gooning onstage.

The following year, the Finn brothers reunited for their 'Finn' project, an album of music written and recorded by the duo, which they toured. It was followed, a year later, by **Recurring Dream**, a greatest hits of Crowded House's material to date. Halfway through the promotional duties for said release, Neil Finn announced he was dissolving the band, telling The Sydney Morning Herald "I didn't feel like I was getting enough out of it creatively to justify making the personal compromises that being in a band entails." Hester immediately fired off a congratulatory fax to his erstwhile bandmate, explaining later, "Neil's been in a band for twenty years, I think that's enough for a bloke".

And so the story of Crowded House drew to a close. There was, however, a coda for dedicated fans, three new songs - **Instinct**, **Not The Girl You Think You Are** and **Everything's Good For You** - recorded especially for the album in Auckland with Froom and Blake. **Instinct** in particular was a strong tune, which could've easily slipped on any of the band's pervious albums, and

featured, as a special bonus, Hester playing drumsticks made of human bones and percussion instruments fashioned from goat's teeth.

But **Not The Girl You Think You Are** was perhaps the sweetest swansong the band could've hoped for. For all the glimmers and references elsewhere, this was their most unabashedly Beatle-esque moment, cooing harmonies and sweeping melodies, a keening chorus, a charming minor-chord verse. Pure classicist pop escapism, the likes of which had been a Crowded House trademark for years. As a cap to a career of sweet, powerful pop music, it was only rivalled by the band's tear-stained farewell performance, at the Sydney Opera House, November 24, 1996.

And so the members of Crowded House went on to pastures new, but these songs remain. Timeless pop music of the highest quality, music which has touched countless thousands through the years, and a testament to the enduring songwriting skills of Neil Finn. Bands like Crowded House come along once in a lifetime; here's eighteen reasons to cherish them when you find them.

Stevie Chick has been a freelance music writer for four years, contributing to Melody Maker, NME, Kerrang!, The Times, the Evening Standard and Sleaze Nation, and is currently a contributing editor of **Careless Talk Costs Lives**. He lives in London and has recently completed work on his book **Don't Stop Now: The Ballad Of Guided By Voices**, the amazing tale of 30-something songwriter Robert Pollard's ascent from school teacher obscurity to indie-rock superstardom.

Don't Dream It's Over

Words and Music by
NEIL FINN

Ebsus2 Bbm/Eb Bbm7/Eb Cm Ab G

Bb Eb Db Fm7 Gm7

Moderately in 2   Capo at 3rd fret

Intro   ¢   **Ebsus2**   **Bbm/Eb**   **Bbm7/Eb**

| / / / / / | / / / / / | / / / / / | / / / / / |

Ebsus2   **Bbm/Eb**   **Bbm7/Eb**

| / / / / / | / / / / / | / / / / / | / / / / / |

Verse 1   **Ebsus2** | |

There is freedom within,

Cm | |

there is freedom without.

Ab | |

Try to catch   the del - uge in a paper   cup.

G

| / / / / / | / / / / / |

Ebsus2 | |

There's a battle ahead,

Cm | |

many battles are lost,

Ab | |

but you'll never see the end of the road   while you're

G | |

trav'ling   with   me.

Chorus 1

A♭		**| B♭**	|

Hey now,   hey   now,   don't

E♭	**| Cm**	|

dream   it's   over.   Hey

A♭	**| B♭**	|

now,   hey   now,   when the

E♭	**| Cm**	|

world   comes   in.   They

A♭	**| B♭**	|

come,   they   come

E♭	**| Cm**	|

to build a wall between us.

A♭	|	|

We know   they   won't win.

G

| /   /   /   / | /   /   /   / |

Verse 2

E♭sus2	|	|

Now I'm towing   my car;

Cm	|	|

there's a hole   in the roof.

A♭	|	|

My possessions are causing me suspicion but there's

G	|	|

no proof.

E♭sus2	|	|

In the paper today;

Cm	|	|

tales of war and of waste,

A♭	|	|

but you turn   right o - ver to the T. V. page.

G

| /   /   /   / | /   /   /   / |

Chorus 2

A♭ | B♭ |
     Hey now,   hey   now,   don't

E♭ | Cm |
     dream   it's   over.   Hey

A♭ | B♭ |
     now,   hey   now,   when the

E♭ | Cm |
     world   comes   in.   They

A♭ | B♭ |
     come,   they   come

E♭ | Cm |
     to   build   a   wall   between   us.

A♭ | | |
     We know   they   won't win.

Interlude

E♭sus2   Cm
| / / / / / | / / / / / | / / / / / | / / / / / |

A♭   G
| / / / / / | / / / / / | / / / / / | / / / / / |

E♭sus2   Cm
| / / / / / | / / / / / | / / / / / | / / / / / |

A♭   G
| / / / / / | / / / / / | / / / / / | / / / / / |

A♭   E♭   A♭   E♭
| / / / / / | / / / / / | / / / / / | / / / / / |

A♭   E♭   D♭
| / / / / / | / / / / / | / / / / / | / / / / / |

| / / / / / | / / / / / |

Verse 3

E♭sus2 | |
Now I'm walking   again

Cm | |
to the beat   of   a drum,

A♭ | |
and I'm counting the steps   to the door of your heart.

G
| /   /   /   / | /   /   /   / |

E♭sus2 | |
Only shadows ahead

Cm | |
barely clearing the roof.

A♭ | |
Get to know the feeling   of   liberation

A♭ | |
and relief.   Hey

Chorus 3

A♭ | B♭ |
now,   hey   now,   don't

E♭ | Cm |
dream   it's   over.   Hey

A♭ | B♭ |
now,   hey   now,   when the

E♭ | Cm |
world   comes   in.   They

A♭ | B♭ |
come,   they   come

E♭ | Cm |
to build a wall between us.

A♭ | |

We know   they   won't win.

| /   /   /   / | /   /   /   / |

       B♭   **E♭**

| /   /   /   / | /   /   /   / |

A♭ |

Don't let them win.

Coda   **A♭** | **B♭** |

Hey now,   *hey*   *now.*

E♭ | **Cm** |

Don't let them   win.

(Repeat Coda to fade)

Chocolate Cake

Words and Music by
NEIL FINN AND TIM FINN

Am7   F   D   G   Am/F#   A7

Em   Em7   D7   E7   Am/C   Asus4

♩ = 115

Intro Am7

$\frac{4}{4}$ | / / / / | / / / / | / / / / | / / / / |

Not

Verse 1 Am7 | |
everyone   in New York   would pay to see Andrew Lloyd

| |
Webber,   may his

| |
trousers   fall   down   as   he   bows to the queen   and the

| |
crown.   I don't

F | |
know what   tune   that the or-chestra   played but it   went

D | G |
by me.   Sickly.   Sen-timental.

Chorus 1 Am7 | |
Can I have another   piece of chocolate cake?

Am/F# | G |
Tammy Baker's got a lot on her   plate.

Am7 | |

Can I buy another cheap Picasso fake?

Am/F♯ | **G** |
Andy Warhol must be laughing in his grave.

Am⁷
| / / / / | / / / / | / / / / | / / / / |
The

Verse 2

Am⁷ | |
band of the night take you to ethereal heights over

| |
dinner, and you

| |
wander the streets never reaching the heights that you

| |
seek, and the

F | |
sugar that dripped from the vi-olin's bow made the child-

D | **G** |
ren go crazy, put a hole in the tooth of a hag.

Chorus 2

Am⁷ | |
Can I have another piece of chocolate cake?

Am/F♯ | **G** |
Tammy Baker's must be losing her faith, yeah.

Am⁷ | |
Can I buy another cheap Picasso fake?

Am/F♯ | **G** |
Andy Warhol must be laughing in his grave. And dogs

A⁷ | **D** |
are on the road. We're all tempting fate. Cars

A⁷ | **D** |

are shooting by   with no   number   plates   and

Em | |
here   comes   Missis   Hairy Legs.

Interlude   **Am⁷**   **Em**   **Am⁷**   **Em⁷**
| / / / / / | / / / / / | / / / / / | / / / / / |

              Am⁷   **Em7**   **Am⁷**   **Em⁷**   **Am⁷** **Em⁷**   **A**   **D⁷**
| / / / / / | / / / / / | / / / / / | / / / / / |
                                                                     I

Verse 3   **Am⁷** | |
saw   Elvis   Presley   walk   out   of   a   Seven   Elev-

en.   That's right.   And a

woman gave birth to a baby and then bowled two-fif-

ty-seven.   Now the

F | |
excess   of   fat   on   your   A-merican bones   will

D⁷ |**G**   **E⁷** |
cushion the impact as you   sink like a stone.

Chorus 3   **Am⁷** | |
        Can I have another   piece of chocolate cake?

Am/F♯   **|G** |
     Tammy Baker.   Tammy Baker.

Am⁷ | |
        Can I buy another   cheap Picasso fake?

Am/F♯   **|G** |

cheap Picasso,   cheap Picasso fake.

Am⁷ | |
Can I have another   piece of chocolate cake?

Am/F♯ | **G** |
Kathy Straker; boy could she lose some weight?

Am⁷ | |
Can I buy another   slice of real estate?

Am/F♯ | **Am/C** |
Liberace must be laughing in his grave.

A^{sus4}
| / / / / / | / / / / / | / / / / / | / / / / / |
                          Ooh.

Am   **G**   **Am**   **G**   **Am**   **G**   **Am**   **G**
| / / / / / | / / / / / | / / / / / | / / / / / |

Coda   **Am**   **G** | **Am**   **G** |
               Can I have another piece of chocolate cake?
(Repeat Coda to fade)

Distant Sun

Words and Music by
NEIL FINN

Eb   Ebsus2   Ab   Absus2   Cm   F9/A   G7

Bb   Fm7   Ab/Eb   Eb/Bb   Abmaj7   G7/D

♩ = 115   Capo at 3rd fret

Intro

| Eb | Ebsus2 Eb | Ebsus2 | Ab | Absus2 Ab | Absus2 |
| 4/4 | / / | / / | | / / | / / |

| Eb | Ebsus2 Eb | Ebsus2 | Ab | Absus2 Ab | Absus2 |
| | / / | / / | | / / | / / |

| Eb | Ebsus2 Eb | Ebsus2 | Ab | Absus2 Ab | Absus2 |
| | / / | / / | | / / | / / |

| Eb | Ebsus2 Eb | Ebsus2 | Ab | Absus2 Ab | Absus2 |
| | / / | / / | | / / | / / |

Verse 1

Eb *(vary chords sim.)* | Ab |
Tell me all the things you would change.   I

Eb | Ab |
don't pretend to know what you want   when you

Cm | F9/A |
come around and spin my   top   time and again,

Ab | G7 |
                    time and again.   No fire

Eb | Ab |
          where I lit my spark,

E♭   **| A♭**   **|**
I am not afraid of the dark,   where

Cm   **| F⁹/A**   **|**
your words   devour my heart,   and put me to shame,

A♭   **| G⁷**   **|**
       put me to shame.   And your

Chorus 1   **B♭**   **| Fm⁷**   **|**
     seven worlds collide,   when-

A♭   **B♭**   **| E♭**   **|**
ever I am by   your side,   and

B♭   **| Fm⁷**   **|**
dust from   a distant   sun   will

A♭   **B♭**   **| E♭**   **|**
shower over   everyone.

A♭/E♭   **| E♭**   **| A♭/E♭**   **|**
                                                  Your

Verse 2   **E♭**   **| A♭**   **|**
still so young to travel so far,

E♭   **| A♭**   **|**
old enough to know who you are,

Cm   **| F⁹/A**   **|**
wise enough to carry the   scars   without any blame.

A♭   **| G⁷**   **|**
      There's no-one to blame.   It's

E♭   **| A♭**   **|**
easy   to forget what you learned,

E♭   **| A♭**   **|**
waiting for the thrill to return.

Cm   **| F9/A**   **|**
Feeling your desire   burn,   you're drawn to the flame.

A♭   **|**
                    When your

Chorus 2   **B♭**   **| Fm7**   **|**
          seven worlds collide,   when-

A♭   **B♭**   **| E♭**   **|**
ever I am by   your side,   and

B♭   **| Fm7**   **|**
dust from   a distant   sun   will

A♭   **B♭**   **| E♭**   **|**
shower   everyone.

B♭   **| Fm7**   **|**
Dust from   a distant   sun   will

A♭   **B♭**   **|**
shower over   everyone. And I'm

Bridge   **Cm**   **E♭/B♭**   **| A♭maj7**   **B♭** **|**
lying on the table   washed out,   in the flood,

Cm   **E♭/B♭**   **| A♭maj7**   **B♭** **|**
       like a Christian fearing vengeance   from above,   I

Cm   **E♭/B♭**   **| A♭maj7**   **|**
don't pretend to know what you want,   but I offer love.

      B♭   **Fm7**   **A♭**   **B♭**   **E♭**
| / / / / / | / / / / / | / / / / / | / / / / / |

      B♭   **Fm7**   **A♭**   **B♭**   **E♭**
| / / / / / | / / / / / | / / / / / | / / / / / |

Chorus 3   B♭ | Fm⁷ |
            Seven worlds will collide,   when-

            A♭   B♭ | E♭ |
            ever I am by   your side,   and

            B♭ | Fm⁷ |
            dust from   a distant   sun   will

            A♭   B♭ |
            shower over   everyone.

Coda   E♭ | G⁷ | A♭maj7 | |
            (on.)   As time slips by

            E♭ | G⁷/D | A♭maj7 | |
                                                         and on and

            (Repeat Coda to fade)

Fall At Your Feet

Words and Music by
NEIL FINN

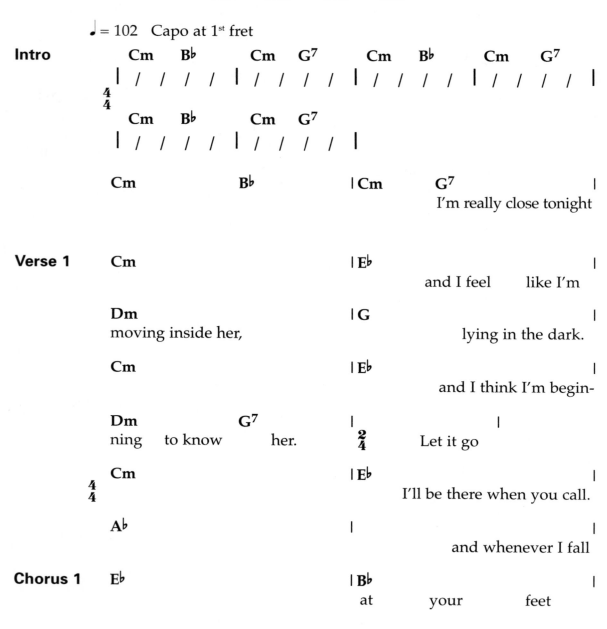

♩ = 102   Capo at 1st fret

Intro
Cm B♭   Cm G⁷   Cm B♭   Cm G⁷

Cm B♭   Cm G⁷

Cm   B♭ |Cm   G⁷ |
I'm really close tonight

Verse 1   Cm |E♭ |
and I feel   like I'm

Dm |G |
moving inside her,   lying in the dark.

Cm |E♭ |
and I think I'm begin-

Dm   G⁷ | |
ning   to know   her.   ²⁄₄   Let it go

Cm |E♭ |
I'll be there when you call.

A♭ | |
and whenever I fall

Chorus 1   E♭ |B♭ |
at   your   feet

```
Cm                              | A♭                          |
                                          you let your tears

E♭                              | B♭                          |
                                 rain        down        on

Cm                              | A♭                          |
      me,                                      whenever I touch

E♭                              | B♭                          |
                            your      slow      turning pain.

Cm                              | A♭                          |
                                    You're hiding from me now,
```

Verse 2

```
        Cm                      | E♭                          |
                                    there's something in the way

        Dm                      | G                           |
            that you're talking.            Words don't   sound

        Cm                      | E♭                          |
            right,                           but I hear them    all

        Dm              G⁷      |                    |
        moving   inside   you.        2       Let it go
                                      4
        Cm                      | E♭                          |
                                     I'll be waiting when you call.
  4
  4
        A♭                      |                             |
                                Hey            and whenever I fall
```

Chorus 2

```
        E♭                      | B♭                          |
                                 at        your       feet

        Cm                      | A♭                          |
                                    won't you let your tears

        E♭                      | B♭                          |
                                 rain      down       on
```

27

Cm | **A♭** |
    me,   whenever I touch

E♭ | **B♭** |
        your   slow   turning pain?

Cm | **A♭** |
                   The finger of blame

Bridge   **E♭** | **B♭** |
    has   turned   upon   itself   and I'm   more

Cm | **A♭** |
    than   willing   to   offer myself,   do you want

E♭ | **B♭** |
    my   presence or need   my   help?   Who

Cm | **A♭** |
    knows where that might lead?   I

E♭ | **B♭** |
    fall.

      Cm   **A♭**
| /   /   /   / | /   /   /   / |

      E♭   **B♭**
| /   /   /   / | /   /   /   / |

Cm | **A♭** |
                   Whenever I fall

Chorus 3   **E♭** | **B♭** |
      at   your   feet

Cm | **A♭** |
             would you let your tears

E♭ | **B♭** |
    rain   down   on

Cm | **A♭** |

    me,   whenever I fall,

E♭ | **B♭** |

                                               ever I fall?

Cm | **A♭** |

                                 You're hiding from me now,

      Cm   **A♭**

| /   /   /   / | /   /   /   / |

                         B♭   **E♭**

| /   /   /   / | /   /   /   / ‖

Fingers Of Love

Words and Music by
NEIL FINN

Gm   F6/9   Dm7   B♭   F   C7   C9   E♭add9

Gm7   Cm7sus4   C9sus4   C   Csus4   E♭add9   Gm6   Dm7(add11)

♩ = 114   Capo at 3rd fret

Intro

Gm

$\frac{4}{4}$ | / / / / | / / / / | / / / / | / / / / |

F6/9   **Gm**

| / / / / | / / / / | / / / / | / / / / |

F6/9

| / / / / | / / / / |

Verse 1

Gm | |
Can you imagine that?   An

F6/9 | |
itch   too   sensitive to scratch,   the

Gm | |
light that falls through the cracks,   an

Dm7 | |
insect   too delicate to catch?   I

B♭ |F |
hear the endless murmer,   every blade of grass that shivers in the

C7 |C9 |
breeze   and the

B♭ |F |
sound, it comes to carry me across the land, and over the sea,

C⁷ | **C⁹** |

                 and I can't   look up.

Chorus 1 $E\flat$**maj9** | **F** |

                fingers of love   move   down,

Gm   **Gm⁷** | |

                 and I can't   look back,

$E\flat$**maj9** | **F** | **C⁷sus4** |

          fingers of love move down.

Verse 2   **Gm** | |

Colour   is   its   own   reward.

F⁶ᐟ⁹ | |

Colour   is   its   own   reward,   the

Gm | |

chiming of a perfect   chord.

Dm⁷ | |

Let's go jumping overboard,   into

$B\flat$ | **F** |

waves of joy and clarity,   your hands come out to rescue

C⁷ | **C⁹** |

me,   and I'm

$B\flat$ | **F** |

playing in the shallow water,   laughing while the mad dog sleeps,

C⁷ | **C⁹** |

           and I can't   look up.

Chorus 2 $E\flat$**maj9** | **F** |

                fingers of love   move   down,

```
Gm                Gm7           |                              |
                                      and I can't   look back,

E♭maj9                          | F                            |
                                  fingers of love   move   down,

C9sus4           C7sus4        | C7            Gm7            |
everywhere.                           And there   is   time
```

Bridge 1
```
E♭maj9                          | F                            |
yet                               to  fall by the way,      from the cra-

Csus4                           | C                            |
dle to the grave,        from the  palace to the gutter,          be-

Csus4                           | C                            |
neath the dyiing rays of the sun,          lie the fingers of
```

Verse 3
```
   Gm                                F6/9
|  /   /   /   /   |  /   /   /   /   |  /   /   /   /   |  /   /   /   /   |

   Gm                                Dm7
|  /   /   /   /   |  /   /   /   /   |  /   /   /   /   |  /   /   /   /   |

B♭                              | F                            |
waves of joy and clarity,         a  fallen   angel   walked  on the

C7                              | C9                           |
sea,                                                    and I'm

B♭                              | F                            |
playing  in  the  shallow  water,    laughing while the mad dog sleeps,

C7                              | C9                           |
                                  and I can't     look up.
```

Chorus 3
```
E♭maj9                          | F                            |
                                  fingers of love   move   down,
```

Gm   **Gm⁷** | |

                 and I can't   look back,

E♭maj9 | **F** |

      fingers of love   move   down,

C⁹sus4   **C⁷sus4** | **C⁷**   **Gm⁷** |

everywhere.   And there   is   time

Bridge 2   **E♭maj9** | **F** |

           yet   for you to find   me,

           Gm | |

                  and all at   once

          E♭add9 | **F** |

      fingers of love   move   down.

Gm⁷   **Gm⁶**   **Gm**

| / / / / / | / / / / / | / / / / / | / / / / / |

Gm   **Gm⁶**

| / / / / / | / / / / / |

Coda   **Gm⁷**   **Dm¹¹**

| / / / / / | / / / / / | / / / / / | / / / / / |

(Repeat Coda to fade)

Four Seasons In One Day

Words and Music by
NEIL FINN AND TIM FINN

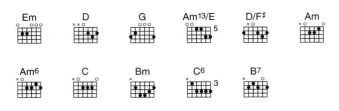

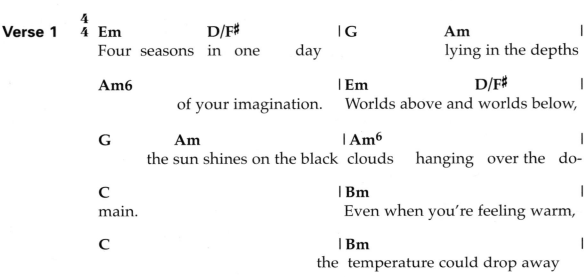

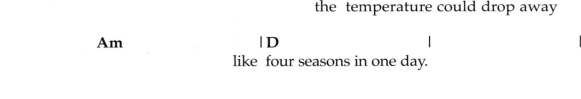

G   Am | Am^6 |
and I will risk my neck again,   again.

C | Bm |
You can take me where you will.

C | Bm |
Up the creek and through the mill.

Am | D |
Like all the things you can't explain,

C | D | G |
four seasons in one day.

Chorus 1   C^6 | G |
Blood   dries   up   like rain,

D | Em |
like rain.

C^6 | G |
fills   my   cup   like

D | N.C. |
four seasons in one day.

                       $^6_4$ $^4_4$
Em   D/F#   G   Am   C   B^7 Em   D/F#
| / / / / | / / / / / / | / / / / | / / / / |

        $^6_4$ $^4_4$
Bridge   G   Am | Em   D/F# |
It doesn't pay to make predictions   sleeping on an unmade bed.

G   Am | Am^6 |
Finding wher-ever there is comfort there is

C | Bm |
  pain   only one   step away.

C | D | G |
Like four seasons in one day

Chorus 2

C⁶ | G |
Blood   dries   up   like rain,

D | Em |
like rain.

C⁶ | G |
fills   my   cup   like

D | N.C. ‖
four seasons in one   day.

Instinct

Words and Music by
NEIL FINN

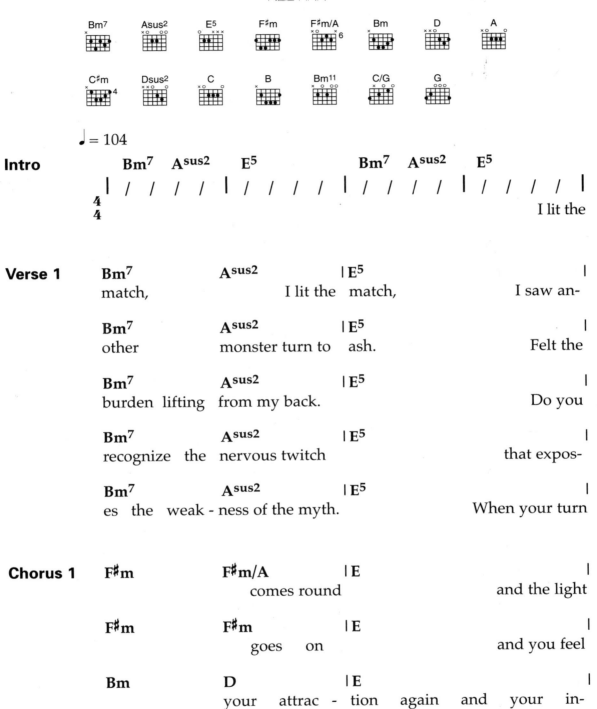

♩ = 104

Intro   Bm⁷   Aˢᵘˢ2   E⁵   Bm⁷   Aˢᵘˢ2   E⁵

| / / / / | / / / / | / / / / | / / / / |

I lit the

Verse 1   Bm⁷   Aˢᵘˢ2 | E⁵ |
match,   I lit the   match,   I saw an-

Bm⁷   Aˢᵘˢ2 | E⁵ |
other   monster turn to   ash.   Felt the

Bm⁷   Aˢᵘˢ2 | E⁵ |
burden lifting   from my back.   Do you

Bm⁷   Aˢᵘˢ2 | E⁵ |
recognize   the   nervous twitch   that expos-

Bm⁷   Aˢᵘˢ2 | E⁵ |
es   the   weak - ness of the myth.   When your turn

Chorus 1   F♯m   F♯m/A | E |
comes round   and the light

F♯m   F♯m | E |
goes   on   and you feel

Bm   D | E |
your   attrac - tion   again   and   your   in-

| **D** | **A** | **\| E** | **\|** | **\|** |

stinct　　can't be wrong.　　　　　　　　　　　　　　Separate the

Verse 2　　**Bm⁷**　　　　　**Asus2**　　　　**\| E⁵**　　　　　　　**\|**

fiction　　　　　　from the fact　　　　　　　　　　　I

Bm⁷　　　　　**Asus2**　　　　**\| E⁵**　　　　　　　**\|**

been　a　little　slow　to　react　　　　　　　　　but it's

Bm⁷　　　　　**Asus2**　　　　**\| E⁵**　　　　　　　**\|**

nearly　time　to　flick the switch　　　　　　　and I'm

Bm⁷　　　　　**Asus2**　　　　**\| E⁵**　　　　　　　**\|**

hanging　by　a　single stitch　　　　　　　　　laughing

Bm⁷　　　　　**Asus2**　　　　**\| E⁵**　　　　　　　**\|**

at　the　ston - y　face　　　　　of gloom.　When your turn

Chorus 2　　**F♯m**　　　　　**F♯m/A**　　　　**\| E**　　　　　　　**\|**

comes round　　　　　　　　and the light

F♯m　　　　　**F♯m**　　　　**\| E**　　　　　　　**\|**

goes　　on　　　　　　　　and you feel

Bm　　　　　**D**　　　　　**\| E**　　　　　　　**\|**

your　attrac - tion　again　and　your　in-

D　　　　　**A**　　　　　**\| C♯m**　　　　　　　**\|**

stinct can't be wrong.　　　　　　　And the

Dsus2　　　　　　　　　**\| C♯m**　　　　　　　**\|**

fearless　come　and　go　　　　　　　where the true

C　　　　　　　　　　**\| B**　　　**A**　　　　**\|**

present lies　　they're calling　down.

E　　　　　　　**\| Bm**　　　**Asus2**　　　**\| E**　　　　　**\|**

They're　calling down,　　　　　　yeah.

Bridge　　**Bm**　　　　　**A**　　　　　**\| E**　　　　　　　**\|**

Cal-

Bm   **A** |**E** |
ling.

          Bm   **A**   **E**

| / / / / | / / / / |

Bm   **A** |**E** |
Laughing at the stony face   of gloom. When your turn

Chorus 3   **Bm^{11}** |**E** |
          comes round   and the light

Bm^{11} |**E** |
          goes   on   and you feel

Bm^{11} |**E** |
          your   attrac - tion   again   and   your   in-

D   **A** |**C/G** |
stinct can't be wrong.

| / / / / | / / / / |

G |**C/G** |
          Cal - ling down.

G |**C/G** |**G** |
          Cal - ling down.

Coda   **C/G**   **G**   **C/G**   **G**

| / / / / | / / / / | / / / / | / / / / |
(Repeat Coda to fade)

It's Only Natural

Words and Music by
NEIL FINN AND TIM FINN

| F | Fsus4 | E♭ | B♭ | Dm | Am |
| C | A7 | B♭ | F5 | E♭add9 |

♩ = 115   Capo at 1st fret

Intro

$\frac{4}{4}$ | **F** / / / / | / / / / | / / / / | / / / / |

Verse 1

F　　　　　　**Fsus4**　　　　|**F**　　　　　　**Fsus4**　　　　|
Ice　　will　　melt,　　　　　water　　will　　boil.

F　　　　　　**Fsus4**　　　　|**F**　　　　　　**Fsus4**　　　　|
　　You　and　I　　　can shake off this　mortal coil,　it's

E♭　　　　　　**B♭**　　　　|**E♭**　　　　　　**B♭**　　　　|
bigger　than　us.　　You don't　have　to worry　about

F　　　　　　**Fsus4**　　　　|**F**　　　　　　**Fsus4**　　　　|
it.

F　　　　　　**Fsus4**　　　　|**F**　　　　　　**Fsus4**　　　　|
Ready　or　　not　　　here　comes　the drop.

F　　　　　　**Fsus4**　　　　|**F**　　　　　　**Fsus4**　　　　|
　　You feel　　lucky when you　know where you are. You know it's

E♭　　　　　　**B♭**　　　　|**E♭**　　　　　　**B♭**　　　　|
gonna come true　　　　here　in　your　arms　I remem-

F　　　　　　**Fsus4**　　　　|**F**　　　　　　**Fsus4**　　　　|
ber.　　　　　　　　　　　　　　It's only

Chorus 1

Dm | |
natural   that I should   want   to   be there

Am | |
     with you.   It's only

Dm | |
natural   that   you should feel the same way too.

Am | |
                It's

Verse 2

F   **Fsus4** |**F**   **Fsus4** |
easy when you don't   try   going   on   first impressions.

F   **Fsus4** |**F**   **Fsus4** |
Man   in   a   cage   has   made his con-fessions now. You've

Eb   **Bb** |**Eb**   **Bb** |
seen   me   at   my worst and it won't be the   last time I'm down

F   **Fsus4** |**F**   **Fsus4** |
there.   I

F   **Fsus4** |**F**   **Fsus4** |
want   you   to   know   I feel com-pletely   at   ease.

F   **Fsus4** |**F**   **Fsus4** |
Read me like a book   that's fallen   down between your

Eb   **Bb** |**Eb**   **Bb** |
   knees.   Please   let me have my way with

F   **Fsus4** |**F**   **Fsus4** |
you.   It's only

Chorus 2

Dm | |
natural   that I should   want   to   be there

Am | |
     with you.   It's only

Dm
natural　　　　　　　　　　　　　　　| 　　　　　　　　　　　　|
　　　　　　　　　　　　that you should feel the same way too.

Am　　　　　　　　　　　| **C**　　　　　　　　　　|
　　　　　　　　　　　　　　　　　　　　　　　　　　It's circum-

Bridge　　**F**　　　　　　　　　　| **A⁷**　　　　　　　|
　　　　　　stantial.　　　　It's nothing written in the sky,　　　and

B♭　　　　　　　　　　　| 　　　　　　　　　　|
we don't even have to　　try.

　　　　　　F⁵
| 　/　　/　　/　　/　| 　/　　/　　/　　/　|

| 　　　　　　　　　　　　|
　　　　　　　　　　　　　　　　　　　　But we'll be

F　　　　**Fsus4**　　　| **F**　　　**Fsus4**　　|
shaking　like　mud,　　　　　buildings　of　glass

F　　　　**Fsus4**　　　| **F**　　　**Fsus4**　　|
sink into the bay,　they'll be under　the　rocks again. You

E♭add9　　　　**B♭**　　　| **E♭add9**　　　　　**B♭**　|
don't have to say.　　　　I know you're afraid.　　It's only

Chorus 3　　**Dm**　　　　　　　　　| 　　　　　　　　|
　　　　　　natural　　　　that I should want　to　　　be there

Am　　　　　　　　　　| 　　　　　　　　|
　　　　with you.　　　　　　　　　　　　It's only

Dm　　　　　　　　　　| 　　　　　　　　|
natural　　　　　　　that you should feel the same way too.

Am　　　　　　　　　| **C**　　　　　　　　|
　　　　　　　　　　　　　　　　　　It's circum-

F　　　　　　　　　　| **A⁷**　　　　　　　|
stantial.　　　　　　　It's something I was born

B♭ | |
    to.   It's only

F | **A⁷** |
natural.   Can I help it if I want

B♭ | | |
    to.   Ooh.

Coda   **F**   **F**ˢᵘˢ⁴   **F**   **F**ˢᵘˢ⁴   **F**

| /   /   /   / | /   /   /   / |

                  Fˢᵘˢ⁴   **F**   **F**ˢᵘˢ⁴   **F**

| /   /   /   / | /   /   /   / |

(Repeat Coda to fade)

Kare Kare

Words and Music by
NEIL FINN, MARK HART, NICK SEYMOUR AND PAUL HESTER

Chord diagrams: Em, Cmaj7, G, Em7, Am7

Chord diagrams: D, Am, Bm, Bm7

♩ = 108

Intro   Em   2/4 Cmaj7   4/4 G
4/4 | / / / / | / / / / | / / / | / / / / |

Verse 1   Em7   2/4 Cmaj7   4/4 G
| / / / / | / / / / | / / / | / / / / |

Em | |2/4 Cmaj7 |4/4 G |
I was standing on a wave,   then I   made the   drop.

Em | |2/4 Cmaj7 |4/4 G |
I was lying in a cave   in the   solid   rock.

Em | |2/4 Cmaj7 |4/4 G |
I was feeling pretty brave   till the   lights went   off.

Chorus 1   Am7 |D |
Sleep   by no   means   comes too soon,

Am |Em |Bm |
in a valley lit by the moon.

Verse 2   Em7   2/4 Cmaj7   4/4 G
| / / / / | / / / / | / / / | / / / / |

Em | | **2/4** | **Cmaj7** | **4/4** **G** |
We left a little dust on his Persian rug.

Em | | **2/4** | **Cmaj7** | **4/4** **G** |
We gathered up our clothes, got the washing done.

Em | | **2/4** | **Cmaj7** | **4/4** **G** |
In a long forgetten place who'll be the first to run?

Chorus 2 **Am7** | **D** |
Sleep by no means comes too soon,

Am | **Em** |
in a valley lit by the moon,

Bm | |
yeah.

Verse 3 **Em7** **2/4** **Cmaj7** **4/4** **G**
| / / / / | / / / / | / / | / / / / |

Em7 **2/4** **Cmaj7** **4/4** **G**
| / / / / | / / / / | / / | / / / / |

Em | | **2/4** **Cmaj7** | **4/4** **G** |
I was standing on a wave, then I made the drop.

Em | | **2/4** **Cmaj7** | **4/4** **G** |
I was climbing up the walls waiting for the band to stop.

Bridge **Cmaj7** | **Em** |
You can say the magic words.

G | |
I've got my sen - sors on,

Cmaj7 | **Em** | **G** |
and this is the only place that I always run from.

Chorus 3 Am⁷ | D |
Sleep   by no   means   comes too soon,

Am | Em |
                          in a   valley lit by the moon,

Bm
| / / / / | / / / / | / / / / | / / / / |

Coda   Em   Bm⁷   Em   Bm⁷
| / / / / | / / / / | / / / / | / / / / |

Em   Bm⁷   Em   Bm⁷
| / / / / | / / / / | / / / / | / / / / |

Em   Bm⁷   Em   Bm⁷
| / / / / | / / / / | / / / / | / / / / |

Em   Bm⁷   Em   Bm⁷
| / / / / | / / / / | / / / / | / / / / |

Em7   C^maj7
| / / / / | / / / / | / / / / | / / / / |

G
| / / / / ||

Locked Out

Words and Music by
NEIL FINN

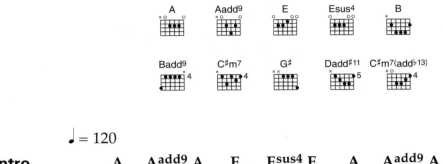

♩ = 120

Intro
A Aadd9 A   E   Esus4 E   A   Aadd9 A   E
4/4 | / / / / | / / / / | / / / / | / / / / |

I've been locked

Verse 1

A   Aadd9   A | E   Esus4   E |
out.   I've been locked in,   but I

A   Aadd9   A | E |
always seem to come back again.   When you're in that

A   Aadd9   A | E   Esus4   E |
room,   what do you do?   I

A   Aadd9   A | E |
know that I will have you in the   end.   And the

B   Badd9   B | A   Aadd9   A |
clouds,   they are crying on you,   and the

A   Aadd9   A | E |
birds are offering up their tunes.   In a

B   Badd9   B | A   Aadd9   A |
shack   as remote as a mansion,   you es-

C#m7 | G# |
cape into a place where nothing moves.   And I've been locked

Verse 2

A   A^{add9}   A |E   E^{sus4}   E |
out.   And I know we're   through   but I

A   A^{add9}   A |E |
can't begin to face up to the   truth.   I waited so

A   A^{add9}   A |E   E^{sus4}   E |
long   for the walls to   crack,   but I

A   A^{add9}   A |E |
know that I will one day have you   back.   And the

B   B^{add9}   B |A   A^{add9}   A |
hills   are as soft as a   pillow,   and they

A   A^{add9}   A |E |
cast a shadow   on my bed,   and the

B   B^{add9}   B |A   A^{add9}   A |
view   when I look through my   window,   is an

C#m⁷ |G# |
altar piece I'm praying to for the   living and the dead.

Interlude

A   E   A   E
| / / / / | / / / / | / / / / | / / / / |

A   E   A   E
| / / / / | / / / / | / / / / | / / / / |

D^{add#11} | |
     Twin valley shines   in the morning sun.

Cm¹³
| /   /   /   / | /   /   /   / |

D^{add#11} | |
     I send a message out   to my only one.

Cm7 | |
                  And I've been locked

Verse 3

A   A^{add9} A | E   E^{sus4} E |
out.   And I know we're through   but I

A   A^{add9} A | E |
can't begin to face up to the   truth.   I waited so

A   A^{add9} A | E   E^{sus4} E |
long   for the walls to crack,   but I

A   A^{add9} A | E |
know that I will one day have you back.   And I

B   B^{add9} B | A   A^{add9} A |
work with the bees and the   honey,   and

A   A^{add9} A | E |
every night I   circle like the   moon,   and it's an

B   B^{add9} B | A   A^{add9} A |
act   of simple   de-votion,   but

C$\sharp$m^7 | G$\sharp$ |
it can take forever when you've got something to prove. I've been locked

D$^{add\sharp 11}$ | Cm^{13} |
out,   and I've been locked

D$^{add\sharp 11}$ | Cm^{13} |
out,   and I've been locked

Coda

     A   E   A   E
| / / / / | / / / / | / / / / | / / / / |
(out.)

(Repeat Coda to fade)

Love This Life

Words and Music by
NEIL FINN

G#m   C#7   D#+   E   F#   B   Bsus4   Esus4

G#m(add9)   Esus#4   D#sus4   D#7   B/F#   C#m   Emaj7   D#m

Intro   Moderately   4/4 | G#m / / / / | / / / / |

Verse 1
| | C#7 | D#aug |
Seal my fate.   I get your tongue in the mail.

G#m | | C#7 | D#aug |
No-one is wise   until they see how it lies.

G# | | E | F# |
Love this life;   don't wait til the next one comes.   Gonna

| | E | D#aug |
pedal my faith   the wheels are still turning round.   Turn round.

Chorus 1   B
                              | |
                       And maybe the day   will   come

Bsus4
                              | |
                       when you'll never have to feel no pain.

Esus2
                              | |
                       After all my complaining,   gonna

Fs | Esus2 | F# |
love this life.   Gonna love this life. Gonna love this life.

Verse 2

| | | **C♯7** | **D♯aug** | |

Love this life.   And so they threw you in jail.   What-

G♯m | | **C♯7** | **D♯aug** | |

ever you've done   it was a million to one.   And don't you just

G♯ | | **E** | **F♯** | |

love this life;   when it's holding you down?   Gonna

| | **E** | **D♯aug** | |

pedal my faith   the wheels are still turning round.   Turn round.

Chorus 2   **B** | |

           And maybe the day   will   come

Bsus4 | |

           when you'll never have to feel no pain.

Esus2 | |

           After all my complaining,   gonna

F♯ | | **Esus2** | |

love this life.   Gonna love this life.   Gonna

F♯ | | **Esus2** | |

love this life.   Gonna   love this life.   Gonna

G♯m   **G♯madd9** | **Esus♯4**   **E** |

love.

        D♯sus4   **Esus♯4**   **E**

| /   /   /   / | /   /   /   / |

       G♯madd9   **G♯m**   **Esus♯4**   **E**

| /   /   /   / | /   /   /   / |

       G♯m   **D♯7**

| /   /   /   / |

Bridge B | |

Here's something that you   can   do

Bsus4 | |

even if you think that I hate

B/F# | B |
you.   Stop your complaining,

Esus2 | F# |
leave me defenseless when you   love this life.   Gonna

Esus2 | F# |
love this life.   Gonna   love this life.   Though you

C#m | F# |
never know why   we love this life.   Gonna

G# | |
love.

Coda   Emaj7   F#

| /   /   /   / | /   /   /   / |

              G#

| /   /   /   / | /   /   /   / |

              Emaj7   D#m

| /   /   /   / | /   /   /   / |

              G#

| /   /   /   /   ‖

Nails In My Feet

Words and Music by
NEIL FINN

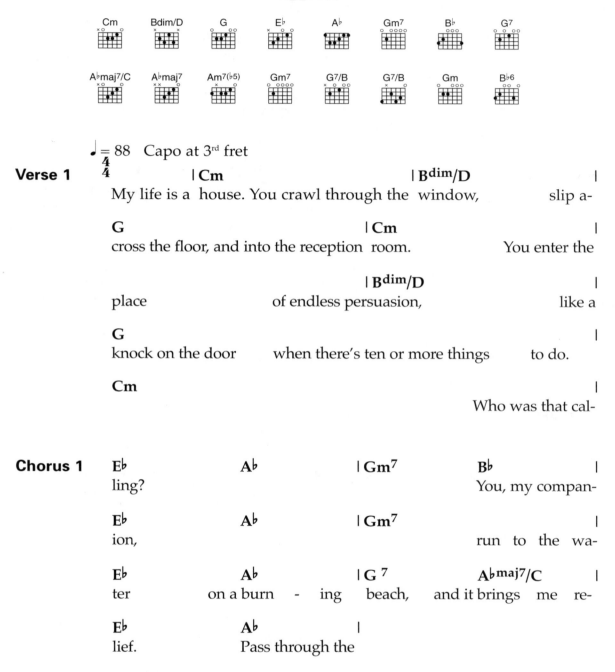

♩ = 88 Capo at 3rd fret

Verse 1 4/4

| Cm | Bdim/D |
My life is a house. You crawl through the window,   slip a-

G | Cm |
cross the floor, and into the reception room.   You enter the

                                       | Bdim/D |
place   of endless persuasion,   like a

G |
knock on the door   when there's ten or more things   to do.

Cm |
                                                    Who was that cal-

Chorus 1 Eb   Ab | Gm7   Bb |
ling?   You, my compan-

Eb   Ab | Gm7 |
ion,   run to the wa-

Eb   Ab | G 7   Abmaj7/C |
ter   on a burn - ing beach,   and it brings me re-

Eb   Ab |
lief.   Pass through the

Verse 2

Cm | B^{dim}/D |
walls   to find my intentions,

G | Cm |
circle round   in a strange hypnotic   state.   I look into

                                   | B^{dim}/D |
space,   there is no connection,   a million

G | Cm |
points of light and a conversation I can't face.   Cast me off one

Chorus 2

E♭   A♭ | Gm⁷   B♭ |
day.   to lose my inhib-

E♭   A♭ | Gm⁷ |
itions,   sit like a lap-

E♭   A♭ | G ⁷   A♭^{maj7}/C |
dog   on a matron's   knee.   Wear the nails   on   your

E♭   A♭ |
feet.

Interlude

    G   Cm^{7sus4}   Gm⁷   Cm^{7sus4}
| / / / / / | / / / / / | / / / / / | / / / / / |

    Gm⁷   Cm^{7sus4}   Gm⁷   Cm^{7sus4}
| / / / / / | / / / / / | / / / / / | / / / / / |

G |
                   I woke up

Verse 3

Cm | B^{dim}/D |
the house,   stumbled in sideways,   the

G | Cm |
lights went on, and everybody screamed surprise.   The savage re-

                                   | B^{dim}/D |
view,   it left me gasping,   but it

G | Cm |
warms my heart to see that you can do it too.   Total surren-

Chorus 2   E♭   A♭ | Gm⁷   B♭/F |
der.   Your touch is so ten-

E♭   A♭ | Gm⁷   B♭/F |
der.   Your skin is like wa-

E♭   A♭/E♭ | B♭ |
　ter   on a burn - ing   beach,

　　　　　　　　　　　　　| E♭   A♭/E♭ |
　　and it brings   me relief,

Gm⁷   B♭6 | E♭   A♭/E♭ |
　　and it brings   me relief,

Gm⁷   B♭6 | E♭   A♭/E♭ |
　　and it brings   me relief.

　B♭6   E♭   A♭/E♭   Gm⁷   B♭6   E♭   A♭/E♭
| / / / / | / / / / | / / / / | / / / / |

　Gm⁷   B♭6   E♭   A♭/E♭
| / / / / | / / / / |

Coda   B♭ | |
                                                        Brings me re-

B♭ | |
lief.   Brings me re-

B♭ | |
lief.

B♭ | |
In the back row and under the stars,   and the ceiling is my floor.

(Repeat last two bars to fade)

Not The Girl You Think You Are

Words and Music by
NEIL FINN

(Chord diagrams: E, Am, B7(11), G#7/B#, C#m, A, G#m, B7, F#m, D#7)

♩ = 95

Verse 1   4/4 **E** | |
You're not   the girl   you think   you

Am | |
are,   no, no.

E | |
They're not his shoes   under your bed,

B¹¹ | |
yeah.

E |**G♯7/D♯** |
He'll take   you places   in his   car

C♯m | |
that you won't   forget,

Am | |
no.

B¹¹ | |
Ah,

Verse 2   **E** |**Am** |
and all the people   that you   know,

E | |
yeah,

                                                             |**Am** |
will turn their head   as you go by.

| B¹¹ | | | |
| | mmm, | |

| E | | G♯7/D♯ | |
| | but you'll be hard | to recognize |

| C♯m | | | |
| | with the top down | and the wind |

| Am | | | |
| | blowing, | |

| B¹¹ | | | |
| | blowing. | |

Chorus 1

| A | | | |
| | He   won't | de-ceive   you | or |

| Am | | | |
| | tell   you   the   truth. | |

| C♯m | | | |
| | Woman   he'll   be   no | |

| G♯m | | | |
| | trouble.   He | |

| A | | | |
| | won't   write   you letters | |

| Am | | | |
| | full   of   excuses. | |

| C♯m | | | |
| | Come on   believe   you   have | |

| G♯m | | | |
| | one   in a   million. | |

Verse 3

| E | | |Am | |
| | You're not the girl   you think   you are, |

| E | | | |
| | yeah, | |

| |Am | | | |
| and someone's standing in your place. | |

B¹¹ | |

           mmm,

E | **G#⁷/D#** |

     The bathroom mirror makes you look tall,

C#m | |

    but it's all   in   your

Am | |

head,   in your

B¹¹ | |

head.

Chorus 2   **A** | |

              He   won't   de-ceive you   or

Am | |

tell   you   the   truth.

C#m | |

Woman   he'll   be   no

G#m | |

trouble.   He

A | |

won't   write   you letters

Am | |

full   of   excuses.

C#m | |

Come on   believe   you   have

G#m | |

one   in a million.

Interlude   **B⁷**   **F#m**

| / / / / / | / / / / / | / / / / / | / / / / / |

         Ah,

      B⁷   **F#m**

| / / / / / | / / / / / | / / / / / | / / / / / |

         ah,

D#7   **E**   **Am**

| / / / / / | / / / / / | / / / / / | / / / / / |

       ah.

B11

| / / / / / | / / / / / |

Chorus 3   **A** | |

He   won't   deceive you   or

Am | |

tell   you   the   truth.

C#m | |**G#m** |

Come on   believe   you   have one.

Am |**Am** |

You're not the girl   you think you are,

E | |

                    oh,

C#m | |**G#m** |

believe   you   have one.

Am |**Am** |

You're not the girl   you think you are,

E | |

                    oh,

C#m | |**G#m** |

believe   you   have one.

Am |**Am** |

You're not the girl   you think you are.

      E

| / / / / / | / / / / / | / / / / / | / / / / / | / / / / / ||

Now We're Getting Somewhere

Words and Music by
NEIL FINN

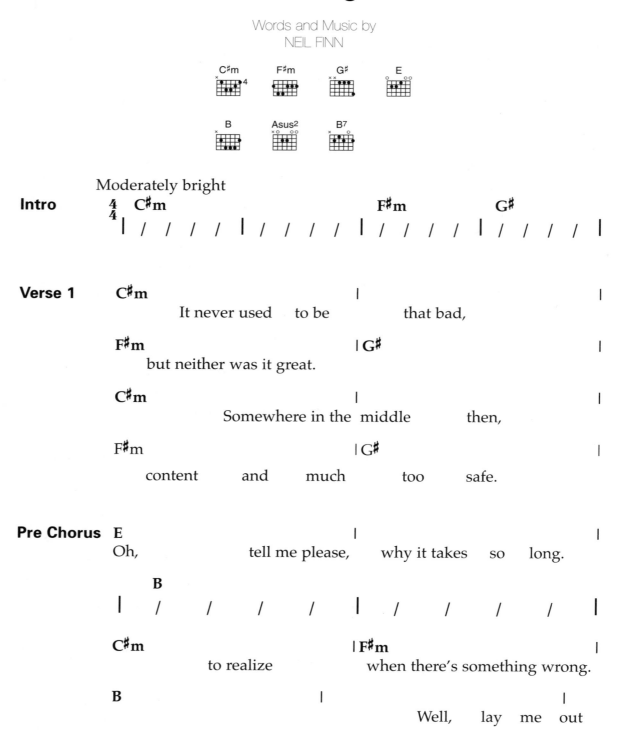

Intro
Moderately bright
4/4 C#m   F#m   G#

Verse 1   C#m
It never used to be that bad,

F#m |G#
but neither was it great.

C#m
Somewhere in the middle then,

F#m |G#
content and much too safe.

Pre Chorus E
Oh, tell me please, why it takes so long.

B

C#m |F#m
to realize when there's something wrong.

B
Well, lay me out

Chorus 1

E | A^{sus2} |

with your heart.   Now we're get-

B⁷ | |

tin'   someplace.   Push me back

E | A^{sus2} |

to the start.   Now we're get-

B⁷ | |

tin'   someplace.   Take me out,

E | A^{sus2} |

let me breathe.   Now we're get-

B⁷ | |

tin'   somewhere.   When I'm with you

E | A^{sus2} |

I don't care   where it is

B⁷ | |

I'm falling.

| / / / / | / / / / |

Verse 2

C[#]m | |

There's money in the Bible   Belt,

F[#]m | |

hugs for Daddy too.

C[#]m | |

Three wishes for eternity,

F[#]m | |

we've   got   some   work   to   do.

Pre Chorus   E | |

Oh,   tell me please,   why it takes   so   long.

          B

| / / / / | / / / / |

```
        C#m                           | F#m                              |
              I believe                     there is something wrong.

        B                                   |
                                         Well,    lay    me    out
```

Chorus 2
```
        E                             | Asus2                        |
                  with your heart.                    Now we're get-

        B7                                |                          |
           tin'         somewhere.                    Push me back

        E                             | Asus2                        |
                       to the start.                 Now we're get-

        B7                                |                          |
           tin'         someplace.                   Take me out,

        E                             | Asus2                        |
                  let me breathe.                    Now we're get-

        B7                                |                          |
           tin'          somewhere.              When I'm with you

        E                             | Asus2                        |
                    I don't care                   where it is

        B7                                |                          |
                  I'm falling.

        |   /      /      /      |   /      /      /      /   |
```

Interlude 1
```
        C#m                            F#m            G#
        | / / / / / | / / / / / | / / / / / | / / / / / |

        C#m                            F#m            G#
        | / / / / / | / / / / / | / / / / / | / / / / / |

        C#m                            F#m            G#
        | / / / / / | / / / / / | / / / / / | / / / / / |
```

Pre Chorus

E | |
Oh, tell me please, tell me what went wrong.

B
| / / / / | / / / / |

C#m |F#m |
'Cause I believe there is something wrong.

B | |
Well, lay me out

Chorus 3

E |Asus2 |
with your heart. Now we're get-

B7 | |
tin' somewhere. Push me back

E |Asus2 |
to the start. Now we're get-

B7 | |
tin' somewhere. Take me out,

E |Asus2 |
let me breathe. Now we're get-

B7 | |
tin' somewhere. When I'm with you

E |Asus2 |
I don't care where it is

B7 | |
I'm falling.

Interlude 2

E Asus2 B7
| / / / | / / / / | / / / / | / / / / |

E Asus2 B7
| / / / | / / / / | / / / / | / / / / |
When you

63

Bridge

E | A^{sus2} |
took me to your room   I,   I swear I

B⁷ | |
said   surrender.   And when you

E | A^{sus2} |
opened up your mouth   I saw the words

B⁷ | |
    fall out.   And though

E | A^{sus2} |
nothing much has changed,   I swear   I sur-

B⁷ | |
render.   And there is pain

E | A^{sus2} |
in my heart,   oh.

B⁷ | |
                           We can choose

E | A^{sus2} |
     what we choose   to believe.

           B⁷
| /   /   /   / | /   /   /   / |

Interlude 2   E   A^{sus2}   B⁷
| /   /   /   / | /   /   /   / | /   /   /   / | /   /   /   / |
(Repeat Coda to fade)

Pineapple Head

Words and Music by
NEIL FINN

F   Bb   Abadd9   Eb   Gm7   Csus4   C   Bb

Bbm/Db   Gm7(b5)   Abmaj7   C7sus4   Ebadd9   Fsus4   Gm9   Gm7(add4)

♩. = 66   Capo at 3rd fret

Intro

| | F   Bb | Abadd9 Eb | F   Bb | Abadd9 Eb |
| 6/8 | | /. /. | | /. /. | | /. /. | | /. /. | |

De-

Verse 1

| F | Bb | | Abadd9 | Eb | |
tective   is   flat,   no   longer   is

| F | Bb | | Abadd9 | Eb | |
always   flat   out,   got the number of the

| F | Bb | | Abadd9 | Eb | |
getaway   car.   Didn't get   very

| F | Bb | | Abadd9 | Eb | |
far.   As

Verse 2

| F | Bb | | Abadd9 | Eb | |
lucid   as   hell,   and these images

| F | Bb | | Abadd9 | Eb | |
moving   so   fast,   like a fever so close

| F | Bb | | Abadd9 | Eb | |
to   the   bone,   I   don't feel   too well.

| F | Bb | | Abadd9 | Eb | |
                                                  And

Chorus 1 | Gm7 | | | Csus4 | C | |

if   you   choose   to   take   that   path,   I will

B♭ |**F** |**B♭m/D♭** |**Gm⁷⁽♭⁵⁾** |

play you like a shark   and I'll clutch at your heart, I'll come

B♭ |**F** |**A♭maj7** |**C⁷sus4** |

flying   like a spark   to inflame   you.

       F   B♭   A♭add9   E♭   F   B♭   A♭add9   E♭

| /.   /. | /.   /. | /.   /. | /.   /. |

Bridge 1   F   B♭ |A♭add9   E♭ |

                  Sleeping   a-lone   for   pleasure   the

                  F   B♭ |A♭add9   E♭ |

                  pineapple   head,   it   spins   and   it   spins,   like a

                  F   B♭ |A♭add9   E♭ |

                  number   I   hold.   Don't   re-member   if

                  F   B♭ |A♭add9   E♭ |

                  she   was   my   friend,   it   was   a   long   time   a-

                  F   B♭ |A♭add9   E♭ |

                  go.   And

Chorus 2   Gm⁷ | |Csus4 |C |

                  if   you   choose   to   take   that   path,   I will

B♭ |**F** |**B♭m/D♭** |**Gm⁷⁽♭⁵⁾** |

play you like a shark   and I'll clutch at your heart, I'll come

B♭ |**F** |**A♭maj7** |**C⁷sus4** |

flying   like a spark   to inflame   you.

       F   B♭   A♭add9   E♭   F   B♭   A♭add9   E♭

| /.   /. | /.   /. | /.   /. | /.   /. |

       F   B♭   A♭add9   E♭   F   B♭m   A♭add9   E♭

| /.   /. | /.   /. | /.   /. | /.   /. |

Bridge 2   F   B♭ |A♭add9   E♭ |

Sleeping   alone   for pleasure the

F   **B♭**   **| A♭add9**   **E♭** |
pineapple   head,   it spins and it spins,   like a

F   **B♭**   **| A♭add9**   **E♭** |
number   I hold.   Don't re-member if

F   **B♭**   **| A♭add9**   **E♭** |
she was my friend,   it was a long   time a-

F   **B♭**   **| A♭add9**   **E♭** |
go.   And

Chorus 3   **Gm⁷**   **|**   **| C^sus4**   **| C** |
                 if   you choose   to take   that path, would you

Gm⁹   **| Gm⁷**   **| C**   **| C^sus4**   **C** |
come   to make   me pay?   I will

B♭   **| F**   **| B♭m/D♭**   **| Gm⁷⁽♭⁵⁾** |
play you like a shark   and I'll clutch at your heart, I'll come

B♭   **| F**   **| A♭maj7**   **| C⁷sus4** |
flying   like a spark   to inflame   you.   I will

B♭m/D♭   **| Gm⁷⁽♭⁵⁾**   **| B♭**   **| F** |
clutch at your heart, I'll come flying   like a spark   to in-

A♭maj7   **| Gm¹¹** |
flame   you.

Coda   F   B♭   A♭add9 E♭   F   B♭   A♭add9 E♭

| | ∕. | ∕. | | ∕. | ∕. | | ∕. | ∕. | | ∕. | ∕. |

                      F   B♭   A♭add9 E♭   F   B♭   A♭add9 E♭

| | ∕. | ∕. | | ∕. | ∕. | | ∕. | ∕. | | ∕. | ∕. ||

Something So Strong

Words and Music by
NEIL FINN AND MITCHELL FROOM

D   Em⁷   Bm   G   G/D   A

Asus⁴   Bm/F♯   D/C♯   G/B   Dsus⁴

Intro Medium tempo

$\frac{4}{4}$ **D**

| / / / / / | / / / / / | / / / / / | / / / / / |

Verse 1   **D**

Love   can   make you weep,

Em⁷   **|D**

    can make you run for cover.

                |Bm

Roots   that   spread so deep

G   **|D**   **G/D**   **D**

    bring life to frozen ground.

Chorus 1 **G**   **|D**

    Something so strong   could   car-

G   **|Bm**   **A**

ry   us   away.

G   **|D**

    Something so strong   could   car-

G   **Asus⁴** | **A**

ry   us   today.

Verse 2

D | |
Turning   in my sleep,

Em⁷ | D |
      love can leave you cold.   The

                                 | Bm |
taste   of   jealousy

G | D   G/D   D |
     is like a lust for gold.

Chorus 2

G | D |
      Something   so   strong   could   car-

G | Bm   A |
  ry   us   away.

G | D |
      Something   so   strong   could   car-

G   Asus4 | A |
  ry   us   today.

Bridge

G   Bm/F♯ | D   D/C♯ |
I've   been   feeling so much older.

G/B   Bm | A |
  Frame me   and hang   me on the wall.

G   Bm/F♯ | D   D/C♯ |
  I've   seen   you fall into the same trap.

G/B   Bm | A |
  This   thing   is happening to us all.

                                    |
               Yeah.

Intro

D		Em7	D Dsus4
/ / / /	/ / / /	/ / / /	/ / / /

D	Bm	G	F♯
/ / / /	/ / / /	/ / / /	/ / / /

Chorus 3

G | D |
Something so strong could car-

G | Bm A |
ry us away.

G | D |
Something so strong could car-

G Asus4 | A |
ry us today. Yeah.

G | D |
Something so strong,

G | Bm A |
something so strong,

G | D |
something so strong,

G | D |
something so strong.

Coda

G	D	G	D
/ / / /	/ / / /	/ / / /	/ / / /

(Repeat Coda to fade)

Weather With You

Words and Music by
NEIL FINN AND TIM FINN

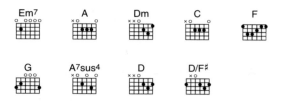

Moderately

Verse 1 $\frac{4}{4}$ **Em⁷**   **A**

| / / / / | / / / / |

Em⁷ | **A**
                                                                  Walking round the

Em⁷ | **A**
room   singing 'Stormy Weather',   at fifty-

Em⁷ | **A**
seven Mount Pleasant Street.   Well it's the

Em⁷ | **A**
same room but ev'rything's diff'rent.   You can fight the

Em⁷ | **A**
sleep   but   not the   dream.

Dm   **C** | **Dm**   **C**
    Things ain't   cooking   in my   kitchen.

Dm   **C** | **F**
    Strange affliction   wash over   me.

Dm   **C** | **Dm**   **C**
    Julius   Caesar   and the Roman Empire

Dm   **C** | **F**
    couldn't conquer   the blue   sky.

```
        G                                    Em⁷
|   /       /       /       /    |   /       /       /       /    |

        A                                    Em⁷
|   /       /       /       /    |   /       /       /       /    |

A                               |
              Ev'rywhere you go
```

Chorus 1 A⁷sus4 | D |
            you always take the weather with you.   Ev'rywhere you go

        A⁷sus4 | D |
            you always take the weather.   Ev'rywhere you go

        A⁷sus4 | G |
            you always take the weather with you.   Ev'rywhere you go

        D/F♯ | G   A |
            you always take the weather,   the weath - er with you.

Verse 2
```
        Em⁷                              A
|   /       /       /       /    |   /       /       /       /    |
```

Em⁷ | A |
                                    Well there's a

Em⁷ | A |
small   boat   made of   China.   It's going

Em⁷ | A |
nowhere on the mantelpiece.   Well do I

Em⁷ | A |
lie like a lounge room lizard,   or do I

Em⁷ | A |
sing like a bird released?   Ev'rywhere you go

Chorus 2 A⁷sus⁴ | D |
you always take the weather with you.   Ev'rywhere you go

A⁷sus⁴ | D |
you always take the weather.   Ev'rywhere you go

A⁷sus⁴ | G |
you always take the weather with you.   Ev'rywhere you go

D/F♯ | G   A |
you always take the weather,   the weath - er with you.

Interlude   Em⁷   A
| / / / / | / / / / |

Em⁷   A
| / / / / | / / / / |

Em⁷   A
| / / / / | / / / / |

Em⁷ | A |
Ev'rywhere you go

Chorus 3 A⁷sus⁴ | D |
you always take the weather with you.   Ev'rywhere you go

A⁷sus⁴ | D |
you always take the weather.   Ev'rywhere you go

A⁷sus⁴ | G |
you always take the weather with you.   Ev'rywhere you go

D/F♯ | E |
you always take the weather,   take the weath-

G   A | D   ‖
-er,   the weather with you.

World Where You Live

Words and Music by
NEIL FINN

Em   D   Am   G   A   F#m   D/A   G/A

F   Fadd9   Fmaj9   Am/G   D/F#   Gsus2/D   Gsus4/D   Gsus2

Intro   Medium
              4/4 **Em**
         | / / / / | / / / / | / / / / | / / / / |

Verse 1   **Em** | |
                   Here's someone now   whose got the muscle.

              D | |
                   His steady hand   could move a mountain.

              Em | |
                   Expert in bed,   but come on now, there

              D | |
         must be something missing.

              Em | |
                   That golden one   leads a double

              D | |
                   life.   You'll find out.   Tell me. I don't

Chorus 1 |**Am**   **G** |
         know   where   you   go.

              D |**G**   **A** |
         Do you climb into space

              D |**Am**   **G** |
         to the world where you live,

```
D                                    | G              A                      |
    to the world where you live?          Oh,        ooh

        Em
    |  /   /   /   /   |  /   /   /   /   |  /   /   /   /   |  /   /   /   /   |
```

Verse 2   Em | |

```
                    So here we lie              against each other.

         D                                  |                            |
                    These four wall              can never hold us.

         Em                                 |                            |
                    We're looking for           wide open spaces

         D                                  |                            |
         high above the kitchen.

         Em                                 |                            |
                And we're strangers here         on our way to

         D                                  |                            |
                    some other place.               But I don't
```

Chorus 2
```
                                    | Am            G                      |
         know   where   you   go.

         D                                  | G            A                      |
                Do you climb into space

         D                                  | Am           G                      |
                to the world where you live,

         D                                  | G            A                      |
                to the world where you live?       Oh,        ooh,

         D                                  | Em        F#m         G           |
                to the world where you live?
```

Bridge
```
         A                                  | D/A                               |
         Friends              come round.               You might

         G/A                                | F                                 |
                    remem-ber               and be sad. Be-
```

A | **D/A** |
hind their eyes is un-

G/A | **F** |
- - famil - iar.

Fadd2 **Fmaj9**
| / / / / | / / / / |

Interlude **Am** **Am/G** **D/F♯** **D** **Am** **G** **D**
| / / / / | / / / / | / / / / | / / / / |

Am **Am/G** **D/F♯** **D**
| / / / / | / / / / |

Am **G** | **D** |
Do you climb into space

Coda **G** **A** | **D** |
to the world where you live,

Am **G** | **D** |
to the world where you live,

G **A** | **D** |
oh, oh, to the world where you live,

G **A** | **D** |
yeah, yeah, to the world where you live,

G **A** | **D** |
to the world where you live,

Gsus2/D | **D** |
to the world where you live,

Gsus2/D | **Gsus4/D** |
to the world where you

Gsus2 | |
live?

D
| / / / / | / / / / ||

Printed by Halstan & Co. Ltd., Amersham, Bucks., England